Accidents Will Happen

It was a cold Friday in April: a college day for Andy Tricker, who was an apprentice mechanic working for his City and Guilds. The afternoon dragged by and Andy decided to skip off a bit early. As his old 50cc bike pulled slowly up the hill the first few drops of rain came down. Andy put his head down as it started to hit him in the face, glancing up at intervals to check the road. Suddenly he got the impression there was a shadow ahead and everything kaleidoscoped together. He realised he was lying under a lorry and decided to move quickly. But, he couldn't move at all and wondered if it was shock. What Andy didn't realise was that he was paralysed.

Accidents Will Happen

Andy Tricker

ANDRE DEUTSCH

First published in 1987 by
André Deutsch Limited
105–106 Great Russell Street, London WC1B 3LJ

British Library Cataloguing in Publication Data

Tricker, Andrew
  Accidents will happen.
  I. Title
  823'.914 [F]   PR6070.R4/

  ISBN 0 233 98095 4

Phototypeset by AKM Associates (UK) Ltd
Ajmal House, Hayes Road, Southall, London
Printed in Great Britain by
Ebenezer Baylis and Son Ltd, Worcester

Contents

Foreword

I wrote this book for my mum, dad and girlfriend, really, when they asked me to write about the worst possible thing that could ever happen to anyone. I was seventeen years old; up until then I'd had different illnesses like measles and chickenpox and different sickness bugs, but I'd never had to go into a hospital. Then, suddenly, coming home from college on my motor-bike, I smashed into the back of a truck and was paralysed completely. Read about my fight to get over my paralysis and to overcome so many difficulties.

Chapter 1
Home and Family

'Andy, it's twenty to eight!'

'Uhm, OK!' I rolled onto my back and looked up at the ceiling. Little did I know then that this view would become compulsory for me in the coming months. I threw back the covers and climbed out of bed. I stood for a minute rubbing the sleep from my eyes. I bent down to pick up my working clothes, then suddenly realised it was Friday and day release. I worked for a large garage in the nearby town of Ipswich as an apprentice mechanic and on Fridays attended the Civic College to work towards getting my City and Guilds. I walked to the cupboard and took my clean things out, opened the door with my left hand and strolled across the landing to the bathroom, where I washed, dressed and relieved myself. After brushing my hair I unlocked the door and went downstairs, through the kitchen and into the lounge-diner where my mum and ten-year-old sister were sitting having their breakfast. Breakfast was about the only time I saw Mum and Louise (Lou for short) during the week. When I got home from work Mum would be out working at her evening job and Lou would be out playing. By the time I got home from Kate's, more often than not they were both in bed.

I finished my cup of tea and stood up to put my jacket on; Mum always got everything I needed ready for me, so it was only a matter of putting things on or picking things up. I zipped up my jacket, chucked my bag over my shoulder, put my helmet and gloves on and shouted, 'Bye, Mum, see you tonight!'

'Have you got enough money?' she called.

As I didn't earn much I could never seem to make it last the whole week and Mum would always be giving me money during the week. 'No, not really,' I answered.

'Here you are, then.' She slipped me a pound as I walked to the back door.

'Thanks, Mum, see you later,' I said as I pushed open the door.

'Money will never burn a hole in your pocket,' I heard her say as I walked down the path.

We had a small garden, a little patio, a pond and a small back lawn with a fence running down either side. The garage was at the very bottom; also, just inside the gate, was a piece of concrete where my bike stood. I had to swing it round and then back it out of the wrought iron gate onto a private road which enabled people to get round to the back of their houses and garages. Beyond the road was a large field where sugar beet or corn were regularly grown.

The houses were only a few years old and I suppose you would describe them as modern terraced homes. There were six in a row and ours was the third from the right. They had a big lounge-diner which ran the complete length; this had two doors leading off it, one to a small kitchen and the other to a small hall and stairs; up the stairs a bathroom faced you and if you turned left there was a small landing with a door facing you which was my parents' bedroom. The room on the right was where my two sisters slept — Lou and my older sister, Joanna, or Jo for short. Finally, to the left, was my bedroom. They were compact and very homely houses.

The whole estate wasn't very big. I suppose there were only about seventy houses and bungalows all told; a butcher's, launderette and a small corner shop which sold almost everything. The estate lay between two small villages: one, East Bergholt, is well known for the famous artist, John Constable; the other, Brantham, not well known but where I had lived on a council estate for the first eleven years of my life and where I had many happy memories.

I kick started my bike, drove through the estate and finally out onto the main road to Ipswich. The road was good and it was only eight miles into town, but by the time I reached the college the cold April morning weather had frozen me to the bone. I put my bike in one of the sheds and walked into the college. I threw my helmet and gloves into my locker and went along to one of the common rooms where I bought a coffee to warm me up.

College wasn't one of my favourite occupations but I had to go if I wanted to get my City and Guilds. I preferred the practical side, the actual working on cars, to the theory — it wasn't that I couldn't do the work: I suppose it was because it was like being back at school. I couldn't wait until one o'clock when I could nip down to the garage, not to work but to pick up my wages — the best time of the week. I signed for my wages and decided to go across the road to the pub for my lunch. As I pushed open the door I noticed a couple of lads from the garage having a game of pool and we exchanged a few friendly jibes. I ordered my lunch: one plate of chips and a half of light ale. I often used the pub during the week for a drink and a game of pool. I was in the team for my local pub and we played most of the pubs in town so I had to keep my eye in. I finished my lunch and just had enough time to get back to College for the start of the afternoon session. I always found that the afternoon sessions dragged on longer than the mornings, and more often than not I would skip the last lesson so as to get round to Kate's just after four.

Kate was a year younger than I was and was just coming up to the last year of her school life. We'd been going out for about four or five years — I remember the first time we

3

started to go out with one another, I was in the second year and she in the first. I was sitting on one of the benches in the playground when Kate's friend, Sally, came over.

'Will you go out with Kate?'

'Kate who?'

'Kate Chorley. She's sitting over there.'

I turned and looked and thought, 'Um, why not?' So I said. 'Yer, OK.' A few minutes later she was sitting beside me and we were holding hands — ah, young love!

'Well,' I said, 'I've got to go now — I've got a dentist appointment.'

'OK,' she said, 'I'll see you tomorrow,' and that was the start of a very long relationship. It eventually got to the point when if either of us were out on our own there was always someone coming up to us and asking where the other one was. We got on great together and were only apart when it was forced upon us either by lessons or sleep. Mind you, it wasn't always great; we split up quite a few times over the five years but always managed to get back together somehow.

As my mates walked across to their next lesson I slipped off to where the lockers were and took out my helmet and gloves. It was only a short walk to where my bike was parked and as I turned the corner there was my mate, Kim.

'Hiya, mate! You going home now?'

'Yer, I'm cheesed off. I thought I'd go early.'

'You couldn't give us a lift, could you?' he said. 'Jane's coming over. We're going to a disco tonight.'

'Yer, if you want, I won't be a minute, just get my helmet.' I slipped my helmet and gloves on and waited for Kim. 'OK, if you're ready? It looks like we might get a wet shirt.'

'Ah, it don't matter.'

Chapter 2
I Can't Feel my Legs

I turned out of the gates and down to the little roundabout at the bottom of the road; a quick right and we were passing through the docks. There was always a terrible smell of burnt corn that filled your nostrils as you went by the malting factory. We turned left at the lights and over a small bridge to another set of lights, straight over those and we were heading out of the town. As we were passing the last few shops on the road out of town, I turned to Kim. 'I bet we don't get home before it rains.'

We passed the service station on the left and reached the bottom of the large hill. My bike was only a 50cc and as we climbed the hill I had to change down a couple of gears. As we went over the crown of the hill the first few spots of rain began to fall. I carried on but it soon began to come down much heavier. There was a bus shelter about a hundred yards up the road and I thought of stopping there until the rain stopped, but I decided against it as I was already quite wet. With two up, my old bike wouldn't pull very well and the fastest she would go was about forty. As the rain started to hit me in the face I gradually started to lower my head and look just a few yards ahead with one eye on the edge of the road: this prevented the rain hitting me straight in the eyes and blinding me completely, but every few moments I would look up just to make sure there wasn't anything in front of me. I had been doing this for about a mile and as I knew the road well I knew that there was a sharp bend coming up soon. As I saw the lines I lifted my head: I didn't want to lean too far over as the road was getting very slippery now.

After we rounded the corner there was the start of a new piece of road. It was much wider than the previous one and enabled people to overtake much easier, but it went down into a slight dip and then there was a small incline up the other side. We had just reached the start of the new road when a large furniture lorry overtook us; it threw up water from the road which descended upon me like a tidal wave, drenching me from head to toe. I cursed the lorry driver for being such a bloody idiot. As we went down into the small dip we got some relief from the rain from a large bank on the right, but as we started up the small incline the rain met us head-on again and I had to lower my head once more. We were just coming to the end of the new piece of road when I thought it was time to look up again.

It was then that I got the impression that there was a shadow in front of me. I looked up — I only had a split second to act and in one flowing movement I wound down the throttle, jammed on my brakes and pushed back with all my might. At the same moment I heard this high pitched noise in my ears and felt as if I had done a complete somersault. It must have only been a matter of seconds before I came to and as I opened my eyes I could see something above me. I realised that I was underneath the back end of a lorry. I thought, 'Crumbs, I'd better get up just in case he decides to drive away.' I motioned my body to sit up but nothing happened. I realised from a previous accident that I could be suffering from shock so decided to relax for a moment. It was then that I started to hear voices, one I recognised as my friend Kim's, the other one said, 'Are you OK?'

'Yer, I think so,' answered Kim, 'but I don't know about my mate. I think he's round the back somewhere.' Then I heard footsteps coming over to where I was. As they came closer I tried to move again but still couldn't. I heard the same voice again. 'Oh God, stay there. I'll get a blanket from the cab.' Then he called to another chap, 'Run to the nearest phone and call for an ambulance.'

'Ambulance, what do I want an ambulance for? I'll be all right in a minute,' I thought to myself.

Kim bent over me, 'Are you all right, Andy?'

'Yer, I'm OK.'

Then I realised I couldn't feel my legs. 'Kim I can't feel my legs! I've tried to move but I can't seem to move an inch!'

Realising now that the first voice had been that of the lorry driver, I heard him say, 'I think we'd better get him out from under there and lay him on this blanket — if we gently lift him together. That's it! Watch his leg, it's caught under the axle. That's it. You'll be all right, mate.'

They laid me down and now I was looking up at a murky grey blue sky. 'Kim . . .' Even talk seemed to be a great effort.

'Yes, mate?'

'Take this helmet off for me, will you? I feel as if I'm suffocating.'

'I don't know if I should, Andy.'

'Come on, Kim, I can't breathe.'

He unbuckled my helmet and gently pulled it back and off my head. The relief was incredible: there was a slight breeze and the odd spot of rain fell onto my face.

There was another voice now and a man leant over me. 'Hello, I'm a doctor. How do you feel, then?'

'I can't move, I can't feel anything except some pain in my arms.'

'Yes, well, you have got two nasty grazes, one on each arm. You're OK, don't worry.' He got up and walked a little way away. I could hear a few people talking and the odd car passing. I heard the ambulance's siren in the distance and I thought to myself. 'Crumbs, by the time I get out of the hospital I'll be lucky if I get up to Kate's at all tonight.'

The ambulance seemed to pull up very close to where I lay. A man in a peaked cap and a grey-blue jacket leant over me. 'OK, young fella, what's your name, then?'

'Andy.'

'OK, then, Andy, your friend tells me you can't move.'

'No, and I can't feel anything either except some pain in my arms.'

'All right then, son, we're going to lift you gently onto this stretcher and then nip you to the hospital.'

They lifted me onto the stretcher and slowly slid me into the back of the ambulance. As I looked up, the grey blue sky was replaced by a bright light in the roof of the ambulance and I could see the blackened window on my right. The man with the cap was sitting on my left and then I heard someone else climb in, 'Kim, is that you?'

'Yer, Andy. I thought I'd come with you.'

I must have been shaken up because the next thing I remember was asking where Kate was; why wasn't she here, she should be with me. We seemed to be going very fast and were soon into the town. I heard the driver say, 'We'd better nip up the road past the bingo hall and then up Franciscan Way otherwise we'll get caught in all the evening traffic.' I could sense the urgency in his voice, then suddenly he blew his horn. 'You bloody stupid cow! You ought to have seen that, Jack, she pulled right out in front of me.' I opened my mouth to ask whereabouts we were when the ambulance came to a halt and the rear doors were flung open.

'OK, Andy,' Jack said as they lowered the stretcher onto a trolley. A cool breeze swept across my face and as I looked up it seemed to have stopped raining. The sight of the sky was short lived and it was soon replaced by bright fluorescent lights. They pushed me along and into what I now know was a small cubicle and pulled a light blue curtain round me. I lay quietly and let my eyes close to give them some relief from the lights.

The next things I heard were the swish of the curtain and footsteps coming to the end of my bed. 'Hello, I'm a doctor.' He was a tall, young coloured doctor and was wearing a white jacket with a stethoscope hanging from his right pocket. 'Let's have a look at you, then. Can you take his clothes off, nurse? I think you had better cut his jumper away.'

'What am I going to put on when I leave?'.

'Don't worry, I'm sure your mum will bring you another one.'

A young nurse leant over me from the left side and began to snip through my jumper until it fell away like a cardigan. She lifted my right arm up and slipped it out of the jumper. Gently, they lifted me up and pulled the jumper away, then they proceeded to remove my trousers. 'OK,' the doctor said. 'Right, tell me if you can feel anything as I touch you? Can you feel this?'

I lay there willing myself to feel his touch.

'Anything now?'

'No.'

He proceeded up the side of the bed asking the same questions until he reached my chest when suddenly I felt a sharp prick.

'I felt that.'

'Good,' he said and I realised he had been pricking me with a pin.

'Right, now I want to have a few X-rays taken to see what damage you've done.' They covered me with a blanket and pushed me out of the cubicle and along a corridor. As they pushed me through some double doors I was greeted by people's voices and the smell of cigarette smoke. I knew from a previous occasion when I had come to the casualty department for a nose bleed that wouldn't stop, that the X-Ray room was right where people sat and waited to be seen.

'OK, wheel him in.'

They manoeuvred me into the correct place and positioned the different pieces of equipment above and around me.

'Right, just lie still while I take a few pictures of you.'

'I can't do a lot else,' I thought to myself. They seemed to take several X-Rays of my head and neck and one of every other part of my body. As they pushed me out of the X-Ray room someone peered over me — Mum.

'Are you all right, love?'

'Yer, but I can't feel my legs.'

Dad was beside Mum now. The orderly who was pushing me spoke. 'I'm sorry but I've got to take him back to his cubicle now,' and their faces were gone. I began to wonder what I really had done to myself.

Unbeknown to me at this time the doctor had asked my mum and dad into his office. 'Please sit down. Your son has damaged his spine but I don't think it's serious and he should be all right in a few weeks. However, I should like the specialist to have a look at him.'

'Hello.' Another doctor. He was standing beside me, a small man beginning to go grey at the temples. He proceeded to do exactly the same tests as the previous doctor with exactly the same answers. 'OK, thank you,' he said and disappeared from sight. A few minutes after he had left me he asked my parents into the sister's office. He never offered them a seat although he was sitting himself.

'I've looked at your son's X-Rays and I've got to tell you he has broken his neck and he will never walk again.'

I remember my mum telling me months later that she looked at Dad: the colour had drained from his face and he tried to lean against the wall for support. Then he spoke, 'Are you sure, doctor?'

'Yes. Well, you parents will buy your children these bloody motor-bikes.'

My mum took hold of my dad's arm. 'Don't worry, dear,

something will work out,' she said, and both their eyes welled with tears.

As the doctor walked to the door he turned to my parents and said, 'I'm trying to arrange for your son to be airlifted by helicopter to Stoke Mandeville in the next couple of days. It is world famous for its spinal unit,' and with that he left my parents in the sister's office. By this time I had been moved to a ward. They had fitted some kind of strap under my chin to prevent me from moving my head, at the same time leaving me able to speak.

I heard footsteps coming over to where I lay and then Mum and Dad leant over me. I could see by their eyes that they had been crying.

'How do you feel now, love?' Mum asked and I said the same thing that I had when I saw them in the casualty department. 'I can't feel my legs, Mum.' I must have said that over and over again in those first few days.

'Don't worry, son, you'll be all right,' Dad said. 'You're just suffering from shock.'

They stayed with me some time, asking me how it happened and comforting me as best they could. I think they must have realised that I was finding it increasingly hard to talk, so they said they had better get home to check Lou was OK and that they would be back in the morning.

The night seemed endless. I lay staring up at the pattern of the light which was given off by the night nurse's small lamp. I would hardly close my eyes when I would be woken by unbearable pain in my arms. I called to the nurse and she came over.

'I've got terrible pains in my arms,' I said.

'I'm sorry, but there is nothing I can give you. It's impossible for me to sit you up so that you can take any pills.' I lay quietly, trying to think of other things than the pain I felt — I thought of walking Kate's dog, Kas, across the fields near where she lived or playing with her on the back lawn. Next morning breakfast and lunch came and finished without my being offered a morsel of food. I had not eaten since the previous lunch time, but the funny thing was I didn't feel at all hungry.

A loud bell rang and I heard countless footsteps walking by my bed and then a familiar voice spoke from the side of the bed: it was Mum. Dad, my brother, Bruce, and his wife, Jackie, were with her.

'Hello, mate! How are you feeling?'

'All right, except for this pain in my arms,' I replied.

They stopped for a while and then said that there was someone else who wanted to see me and that they would come again tomorrow. Bruce and Jackie had travelled all the way from Newmarket. 'How nice,' I thought.

Then I heard just one person's footsteps coming across the tiled floor. 'Hello, darling.'

It was Kate. She leant over and kissed me. 'Don't worry, babe, you will soon be out of here.' Her face had a worried look on it and it was as if she was saying the words to reassure herself as much as me. She lifted the sheet to find my hand. I could not tell if she had succeeded as I felt nothing. A small smile came upon her face, and I knew this small action had given her comfort. I knew by the way she spoke that she was choosing her words very carefully, but she spoke of how she would visit me every evening and how I'd soon be better. I wanted to believe her so much. I looked at her: she was really pretty, with hazel eyes and short, light brown hair and a perfect complexion; she had a small genuine beauty spot on her right cheek near the corner of her mouth; she wasn't very tall but was well put together. Looking at her standing there the emotion was too much and I had to blink several times to prevent myself from crying. We chatted for a bit longer and then my mum and dad came back for the last ten or fifteen minutes of visiting time.

I know I had some more visitors in the evening, but in those early days I seemed to drift in and out of semi-consciousness. I do know that I had another sleepless night. The following afternoon I had more visitors than the previous day. There were my parents, my brother and his wife, my two married sisters and their husbands, my younger sister and her boyfriend, Tim; Kim (who was on my motorbike with me at the time of the accident) and his girlfriend, Jane; my old friend, Brynly, and finally Kate. There were four or five of them standing around my bed at one time. I was pleased to see them but by the time the visiting was over I was very tired. I remember Mum, Dad and Kate coming back in the evening. It was then that they told me I was going to be flown to Stoke Mandeville hospital the following morning as long as the weather was good enough. I was very apprehensive about leaving Ipswich hospital, my family and friends, but at the same time I was beginning to realize I'd hurt myself much more than I had first thought. 'Is it far? You will still come and visit me every day?' I asked. Both my parents and Kate said they would. The answer to the first part of my question would not become known to me until many months later. I do remember a nurse saying to Kate, though, 'If your boyfriend is going to Stoke Mandeville, you'll never see him again,' which at the time must have frightened the life out of Kate as none of us had ever heard of the place.

Those three days in Ipswich seemed very long. I wasn't moved at all but was well looked after. Now it was Monday morning — the day I was to leave. I still hadn't eaten and breakfast had been and gone. The police constable who was called to the accident had been and taken the particulars about it. Then a friendly face appeared beside my bed; it was my Aunty Mary. She was a District Nurse. She didn't stay long but tried to reassure me that everything would be all right. Then Dad arrived. He tried to jolly me along by telling me it wasn't every day you got the chance to fly in a helicopter. He had come in the hope that he might be allowed to come with me to make the journey less daunting for me, while Mum travelled down by car, thanks to the generosity of Jeff, a friend of Dad's. The morning crept on until, at last, a nurse came over and told us that the helicopter would be delayed as there was too much mist and cloud for it to take off. If all went well it should arrive about 11.00 am. As it got nearer the time, we heard it had been put back yet another hour.

The time seemed to drag terribly and I could see the tension building up in the people around me. A young chap leant over and offered me a cigarette. Although I had been smoking since I was eleven something told me to say no: 'Thanks, but I don't think I'd better.' He smiled and then drew back from the bed. Just then there was a rumble overhead as the helicopter passed over the hospital. My dad asked where it would be landing. 'Oh, there's a school across the road and it's going to land on their playing field.'

A few minutes later two men came into the ward dressed in their flying gear. The sister asked if it would be OK if my dad came with me. 'Of course he can,' the officer replied and Dad nipped off to phone Mum. 'OK, then.' They lifted me onto a trolley stretcher.

'All right then, son, we're going to strap this contraption right over you; it's nothing to worry about; it's just to make sure you're jolted as little as possible.'

The 'thing' was laid on top of me and straps were pulled round me and buckled tightly. I was completely encased, with only my eyes and mouth left free. Dad leant over me. 'Don't worry, Andy. I'm here with you, mate.' Then they slowly pushed me down the corridor and lifted me into an ambulance.

No sooner was I in it but they were taking me out again. I could hear hundreds of young children's voices shouting and laughing as they wheeled me to the helicopter. Then, very gently, they slid me in my encased stretcher into the helicopter. Two or three people climbed in and Dad was one of them. 'OK, Mr Tricker, if you sit there you will be fine.'

'A lady's voice,' I thought to myself, when a young girl in uniform leant over me. 'We're just going to strap your stretcher down then we will be off. You won't feel a thing.'

Then came the sound of someone turning the ignition on and the sound of the rotary blades beginning to turn. The lady was right: I didn't feel us lift up, only the rush of air through the doors which must have been left open. I wondered, 'What happens if the straps break — I will shoot right out of those doors.' The journey seemed very short. Dad told me later it took about three quarters of an hour. When you think it took Mum three and a bit hours by car you can appreciate how long a journey it really was. The landing was just as smooth: I didn't realise we were down until the sound of the rotary blades began to slow down and eventually stop. Then they unbuckled me from the helicopter and carefully lifted me out and back onto yet another trolley.

Chapter 3
Welcome to Stoke Mandeville

A middle-aged lady with short dark hair and a Scottish accent leant over me and said, 'Welcome to Stoke Mandeville.'

I thought, 'Silly woman, anybody would think I had come to a holiday camp.'

I was pushed along what I thought must be some sort of pathway before we reached the hospital doors. As I went through, the warm air hit me. 'We are now going past the hydro-swimming pool. You will be coming up here in a few weeks for a nice swim.'

Still only being able to look upwards all I could see was the chipboard ceiling which, every few yards, was broken up with square sky lights. They carried on pushing me along this corridor, then turned to the left along another corridor. As they slowed and turned into the ward I was greeted with the sound of voices, music and even a television. They manoeuvred my stretcher and removed the contraption which had been put over me during the journey. Oh, that felt good! It was as if someone had come and let me out of a cage. A lady in nurse's uniform leant over me; she had lovely red hair and wore glasses but was only in her late twenties.

'Hello. I'm Sister Shilton. We're going to lift you off this stretcher and put you in a bed.' She called three men, by name, to come over. They spaced themselves at different stages down my side. The sister took hold of my head and the men slid their arms under me. 'OK, after three — one, two, three, lift.' As they lifted me they pulled me towards them and clutched me to their chests. 'Pull the stretcher out. Right! Now lay him down.' After being suspended in midair even for that short time it was a relief to be brought back down to earth — although my head wasn't sure where it was: I had to breathe deeply to prevent myself from passing out.

'Hello there! My name's Dr Silver and this is Dr Bash.' The speaker was a man of medium height with little hair, while the other was a tall, black man.

'Let's have a look at you, then,' Dr Silver said and they proceeded to do many tests. The pin was employed again, with the same negative answers until they reached my chest. They then began hitting me with a reflex stick at various points — knees etc. When they came to my arms I told them about the pain that I had. 'Oh good,' they replied, 'good.' I thought, 'You're not the one who's suffering with it.'

Then they took my blood pressure. Eventually they covered me up and disappeared behind the curtain. I could sense that the level of noise had dropped since I first came into the ward.

I was staring at the ceiling at what looked like a stain when the curtain flicked open: it was Doctor Silver again. 'We are going to put some callipers into your head. It's nothing to worry about. It's to keep your neck straight and to take the weight off your head so it can heal.'

I was now on the move again — down to the surgery. They gave me a local anaesthetic and began to shave the hair at my temples; then they cut the skin on either side. The next thing that was employed was a small drill which ground into both temples; finally they screwed in the callipers. These were described to me later when I returned to the ward. They meet in the middle where a cord is fastened which runs over a little pulley wheel fastened to the end of the bed. Several large weights hang from the end of the cord. I thought I must look like that monster which had bolts coming out of his neck, only mine were coming out of my head.

Whilst all this was going on Mum and Dad had been advised to go down to the hospital canteen. I was told later that when they entered the ward the sister had asked them into her office. 'Sit down, Mr and Mrs Tricker,' she said. 'Now, Andrew has had callipers fitted into his head. They are not as bad as they look and are helping his neck to heal, but for someone who has never seen them before they look pretty frightening. Please try not to show your fright for Andrew's sake.' As Mum and Dad came round to the side of the bed Mum tried to smile but I could see that at that moment it was the last thing in the world she wanted to do. They both pulled up chairs and with different words of encouragement, tried to lift my spirits. While they sat talking to me Doctor Silver appeared at the bottom of my bed.

'Mr and Mrs Tricker, I wonder, would you step into my office for a few moments.'

They got up from their chairs and walked into his office; a sliding door was pulled across to prevent me from hearing their conversation, but months later Mum told me what he had said.

'Sit down, please, Mr and Mrs Tricker. Andrew has had a very serious accident and has damaged the sixth vertebra in his neck and has also damaged his spinal cord — to what extent at the moment we cannot say. I must tell you that your son could die at any time in the next two weeks. Now, you can stay at a hostel just over the road if you want, or have you got other people to think about back home?' The news that I could die had not crossed their minds until that moment and was another terrible shock to them. They knew it was impossible to stay at the hostel as there was no one at home to look after Lou: they decided that they would travel back and forth each day.

My parents returned to their seats beside my bed and began to chat again. I asked what the Doctor had said. 'Oh he was telling us what damage you had done to your neck and why they had to put those callipers in you.' I remember they sat talking to me for quite a while. The time had crept on when at last Dad said they had better make a move for home as it would be half-past nine before they got back. They promised to come again in the morning.

As they got up my eyes filled with tears, but I bit my tongue to stop myself from crying in front of them. Mum leant over and kissed me and Dad squeezed my hand. As they turned I knew they too were close to tears. Although there were other people in the ward, in that bed I seemed to be cut off from everything around me and I could not stop the tears from creeping out from the corners of my eyes and running down my cheeks. 'God help me, please,' I cried out in my mind. 'Please make me well.'

I lay there quietly and from time to time a nurse would come over and check that I was all right. The evening drifted on to night. I managed to sleep a little but was woken from time to time by shouts for a nurse further down the ward. Morning arrived very early in hospital, I was finding out. An orderly came to my bed.

'Wash?'

'Sorry?' I said.

'Do you want face and hands washed?'

'Oh crumbs,' I thought, 'fancy having to have someone to wash your face and hands,' but before I could say yes or no he had soaped the flannel and proceeded with the job in hand. He then took out my toothbrush.

'How will I spit out the paste?' I asked.

'When your teeth have been brushed, spit out into the bowl, sip some water through this straw and spit again.'

It was very humiliating to have to have someone wash me and made me feel so helpless. Breakfast came, but there was still nothing for me. Now everyone was awake. It was the signal for all radios to be put on and their deafening sound filled the ward. After breakfast was finished it was time for all those in bed to have a blanket bath. Off went the sheets. I lay there starkers, while nurses and orderlies washed me from chest to toe. If I thought having my face washed for me was humiliating, this was beyond comparison. After being washed I had to be lifted and the pillows I lay on were puffed up to prevent me from getting pressure sores. This, I found, would now become a part of my daily routine. Patient washed and sheets changed, the band of nurses and orderlies moved on to the next person in bed.

I lay there listening to the different sounds and voices in the ward and the records blaring out of the radio. The next thing I knew I heard a voice: 'Andy!' It was Mum and Dad — they were back.

'Hello, Mum, what time is it?' I asked.

'Just gone twelve, love. How are you feeling today?'

'Not too bad,' I replied.

'Jo, Tim, Lou and everyone send their love.'

They pulled up a chair each and chatted to me about what people had been doing to help them. 'Chris and Terry are going to look after Lou until we get back in the evenings and Chris has been baking cakes and doing the shopping, so I've got nothing to worry about.' Our conversation was only interrupted when the nurses came to turn me. I was now in a bed which, with a touch of a button, would tilt over to a forty-five degree angle. There I would be for two hours and then I would be turned onto my back, then onto the other side. This way the pressure would not be in one place for too long and I would be prevented from getting pressure sores. These in themselves can kill you. There was no advantage in any of the three positions. On my back, I could see nothing but the ceiling and when turned onto my side I had to endure the pain of the chin pad which was there to stop my head from moving. After a little while it would begin to cut into my chin until the pain was unbearable. The one advantage of being on one side was that I could see down the ward if I was on my left side. There were rows of beds on either side and a television on a shelf very high up so that everybody could see it, although where my bed was I could only just make out the colours. My mouth was very dry and I asked Mum if she would go and ask the doctor if I could have a drink. 'I'll go,' Dad said, getting up from his seat, and disappeared from sight. Mum carried on chatting and I asked when Kate would be coming to see me.

'Well, Doctor Silver thinks it's best if you don't have any other visitors except me and your dad for the next few days because he doesn't want you tired out.' I wasn't capable of arguing and let the matter drop.

A new face came to the edge of the bed: it had blonde, curly hair and blue eyes and was smiling.

'Hello, my name's Jane. I am going to be your physiotherapist.' Not only would she be my physiotherapist over the next months, but also the one I could turn to at my lowest; the one who would motivate me to try and do things I did not think I was capable of at that time — and the only person I could confide in about my biggest fear — what the future might hold for me. 'Do you mind if I have a look at you?' she said.

'No, of course not,' I replied.

My mum asked if she wanted her to go.

'No, you're OK.'

She started with my arms, bending them from the shoulder and then the elbows and asking me to try and move them on my own. They were still very painful and I could not even lift them off the sheet. She then began to bend my wrist back and forth and bend and straighten each finger.

'We've got to keep your limbs and joints moving while you lie in bed for several reasons: one, so that your muscles and joints keep supple; another to keep them moving, so if messages do get carried through your nerves from your brain they will remember what they have got to do. If you had broken your spinal cord completely, though, there would be no way the messages could get through.'

After finishing with my arms she moved onto my legs,

bending them up from the knee and hip; she then moved down to my ankle and finally my toes. She covered my legs up again and said that she would return the next day. After she left Mum, Dad and I seemed lifted by her visit.

'That was good, wasn't it, Andy?' they both said and I too was pleased by her arrival.

'Yer, it's really good. I feel now that this place is going to help me get better.'

Dad also told me that the Doctor had said it would be all right if I had a drink — that was two good things that had happened in one day.

It was time for Mum and Dad to leave again and, although I was pleased with what had happened during the day, once they had gone the feeling of being alone again crept upon me. I could hear people chatting down the far end of the ward, and when I was turned to face down the ward I saw two large tables where people who were out of bed and in wheelchairs were sitting waiting for their evening meal. As I watched them sitting there I thought to myself, 'By the time I get out of bed I will be all right and won't need a wheelchair. My legs will start moving again soon.' And then I wondered when I would be allowed to eat again. 'Soon, I hope.'

A nurse came over to my bed and introduced herself. 'Hello, my name's Ann.' I suppose she was about forty. She had brown hair and she reminded me a bit of my mum. She was bigger than Mum, but she had the same friendly warmth. She asked where I came from and what I did and so on. It was really nice to chat to her, but when the food trolley arrived she had to go. One of her jobs as an auxiliary nurse was to dish the food out, and then feed the lads in bed who couldn't use their arms. I returned to my own little world, closing my eyes and trying to think what I would be doing if I were back home. I would have been home from work by now, had my tea and a bath, changed and would probably be down at 'The Grange'. 'The Grange' was a caravan site near where I lived, and I played pool there. It had a really smart club and all my mates got together there. We would have a few games and a drink, then I would push off to the youth club where I would meet Kate and another group of friends. I am not saying I was liked by everyone because I know I wasn't, but I think I got on with most people. The thing I liked best was just to be out and about. Mum always said, 'The only time you see Andy at home is at meal times and when he's asleep' — I'd been that way ever since I can remember. When I was seven or eight Mum would always have to call me half a dozen times before she could get me in, and when I was fourteen and going to discos and things I wouldn't get in until midnight. I just liked being out and about. I couldn't stand being indoors for any length of time. Anyway, enough of reminiscing about what I would be doing tonight. After being at the youth club I would go back to Kate's for coffee and something to eat. I would leave Kate's at about eleven and finally get home and into bed by about half-past.

While I lay there dreaming about home, I must have fallen asleep as the next thing I knew was that somebody was touching my shoulder. I opened my eyes, forced to return to reality: it was one of the orderlies. 'We have come to turn you,' he said. The orderlies were mainly foreigners and always very friendly. They pressed the button on my bed and turned me back onto my back. I was staring at the ceiling, when something banged into my bed. 'Sorry,' I heard a voice say. 'Must be someone in a wheelchair,' I thought, 'knocking into my bed by accident.'

The night dragged on and I listened to the different noises in the ward: there was the sound of someone clearing his throat, the rustle of the night nurses turning the pages of a book and the voices of the two orderlies chatting to each other. At last I dropped off to sleep, only to be wakened so they could turn me again. This continuous turning day and night every two hours would become a daily routine from now on.

Morning arrived and with it the same pattern as the

previous day: first my face and hands were washed; then breakfast was served (but still nothing for me); then came the dreaded bed bath and being lifted into the air so they could change the sheets and puff up the pillows I was lying on. This was followed by the doctors' round. Dr Silver, Dr Bash and the sister would stand round my bed and discuss any improvement. It was on this second morning that I asked if I might have something to eat. 'Did you manage with a drink yesterday?' Dr Silver asked, and I replied that I had. 'Well, all right. Start with a little something at lunch time and see how you get on.'

'Oh good,' I thought as by now it had been four days since I had eaten. After the doctors' rounds Jane (my physiotherapist) arrived to manipulate my limbs: first my arms, hands and fingers and then on to my legs, feet and toes. By the time she had finished Mum and Dad had arrived and it was nearly lunch time. I told them the good news: that Dr Silver said I could try a little food. This seemed to cheer them up no end. Lunch time arrived and I was lucky to be on my side, as this made eating that much easier. But it also brought a terrible feeling of helplessness, as Mum had to cut up each mouthful and then put it in my mouth. I think it must have been just as heartbreaking for her as, after she had given me the third mouthful, our eyes met and I could not stop myself from crying.

'Oh Mum, I can't take much more of this. Please God help me,' I said out loud, the tears running down my cheeks.

'Andy, don't cry. It won't always be like this, you'll see,' Mum said as she wiped the tears from my eyes.

I tried to pull myself together by telling myself not to be so stupid and to act my age. I wasn't a child. 'I am seventeen,' I said over and over again in my head.

Mum and Dad sat with me in the afternoon and only got up when either of them wanted to go to the loo or if I had to be turned. They chatted for a few minutes and then just sat there quietly. During the several hours that they were with me they changed places so that first one could hold my hand

and then the other. Later in the afternoon Jane returned to put me through my paces once again. After she had finished my parents moved back to the side of the bed. It was between six and seven o'clock when they began to make a move so that they could be home just before ten. I think this was the worst part of the day: knowing that once they had gone I would be alone again, and knowing also that they were going to the one place I longed to be.

Chapter 4
Early Days

These first few days in Stoke Mandeville slipped by, each day following the same pattern as the previous one, my parents arriving and leaving at the same time every day. By Friday, my appetite had returned, although I still hated having to be fed. Jane had been coming in twice daily and through the course of the week the pain in my arms had subsided and I was able to move both of them a fraction of an inch with a great deal of effort. It was on Friday afternoon that Mum asked if it would be all right if Kate came up the following day. Sister Shilton said it would. I still didn't like the thought of my parents leaving that night, but now I had something to look forward to the following day.

I was lying on my side facing the wall when I caught a glimpse of Kate as she came into the ward.

'Hi, babe,' she said as she leant over and kissed me. Then she sat down and took hold of my hand.

'What do you think of the callipers, then?' I asked.

'They don't worry me, babe. If they're going to help you get better, I don't care what you look like,' she said.

We carried on chatting, and she told me all about the things that had been happening back home and all the people who had sent their love and hoped I would soon be well again. She told me how good our different friends had been to her: going round and talking to her about all sorts of things to take her mind off what had happened.

Mum and Dad came to my bed — they had been for a cup of tea so that Kate and I could have a little time on our own. They pulled up a chair each and then asked the usual questions: how was I feeling and what had happened while they had been away? They asked me these questions every day they came and after my answers told me all that had happened to them: about the different neighbours who had left tins of food at the front door and who had offered to do the washing and ironing or anything to give Mum and Dad less to worry about. They sat with me all the time except for the usual interruptions when I had to be turned. The hours slipped by and it got near the time when they would have to leave. I knew it was going to be even harder to say goodbye this time. Mum and Dad left first leaving Kate and me to say our goodbyes alone. I wanted to say, 'Please stay, Katie,' but I couldn't get the words out. She stood up and leant over and kissed me. 'I'll come up again tomorrow, babe.' I wanted to put my arms around her and just hold onto her, but I knew I couldn't. She walked away and out of sight.

I closed my eyes tightly and screamed within myself, 'Oh God, what have I done to deserve this?' But no one answered my question — instead I opened my eyes only to look up at the ceiling once again.

The days passed slowly by and after about a fortnight more and more people were allowed to come and see me; this was a good thing in many ways as those first two weeks had taken their toll on my parents; my dad was physically tired from constantly driving hundreds of miles and both my parents were mentally tired from worrying whether I would be alive or dead when they returned the following day. Their hair had turned grey and their faces bore the telling lines of sleepless nights and constant heartache. It wasn't until many months later Mum told me that if it hadn't been for my dad's friend, Terry, who lived a few houses away,

Dad would have had a nervous breakdown. Terry would come over and find Dad just sitting staring at the wall. He'd make him get up and go for long walks and talk out all the things he was holding within himself. He helped him to break down and cry so as to get rid of all the heartache he felt inside. More often than not Terry would come up to see me with my parents to give Dad a break from the driving. As soon as I was allowed other visitors Mum and Dad didn't have to come up every day and this made things a lot easier for them.

During those early weeks in bed I was never short of visitors; someone would arrive nearly every day. When you think how far they had to travel it was incredible. My brother came every Wednesday, my parents came on Tuesday and again on Sunday and they would bring Kate and Lou up with them. The rest of the week either my sister, Judy, and her husband, John, would come one day and Jo and her boyfriend, Tim, would come another. On the remaining days different friends would arrive over the weeks: either work mates or friends from home. If I hadn't someone coming to see me nearly every day I don't think I would have been able to get through.

All the time I was in bed I built up a strong relationship with Jane, my physiotherapist. As she manipulated my limbs I would bombard her with countless questions: when would I get back the use of my body? How seriously was I hurt? What could I do to make my limbs work again? Did she think I would walk again and so on? She would always answer me in such a way as not to give me false hopes, but on the other hand not to discourage me. She would also have to cope with whatever kind of mood I was in: she could tell if I was having a good day or bad; when I wanted to talk or when I didn't care whether she was there or not. As she worked my limbs she would tell me about the other patients she had to look after and all about where she lived, the house she was sharing and where her parents' home was. I felt so at ease with her that when she wanted me to try and move my legs or fingers I wanted to do it for her as well as myself. She was always smiling when she came, although sometimes I think there must have been things that got her down. But she never burdened me with her own problems.

It was on the second of May that I had been flown to Stoke Mandeville and by June the third I was still lying flat on my back. The days in between had passed with the same repetitiveness of pattern that had been set on the first day I arrived, although by now I had come to terms with the fact that the hated bed baths and constant turning were in my best interest.

I had been moved further down the ward. This in itself meant that I was improving: the people who were down at the far end of the ward where the french doors were and where the television was were able to get out of bed and were approaching the time when they would be allowed home, so you measured your improvement by how far down the ward you were. I had also grown used to the constant pulling from the weights that were attached to the callipers in my head, although I could not get used to the jaw pad which was used when I was turned onto my side. It would be fine for a little while, but after about half an hour my jaw would begin to ache until it became very sore and tender. My arms had improved greatly over the first month and I no longer had the humiliating task of asking Mum if she would blow my nose for me. Although my arms had improved my fingers still remained paralysed and I still had to rely on someone to feed me — until this particular morning, June the third, when one of the occupational therapists came to see me. She produced a strap which fitted round my hand, then she put the handle of a fork into it and I could hold the fork without having to grip it. I tried it out that lunch time. Although I still needed someone to cut my food, from now on I would be able to feed myself. This job of feeding myself (which I had taken for granted since I could remember) became the most difficult task I had to do over the next weeks. My food would be stone cold by the time I had finished as it took me several attempts at forking to get every mouthful in. Peas were a non-starter and more ended up in my bed than in my mouth! I seemed to improve as the days passed, but one day the terrible thought came to me that I would always have to use a strap to feed myself. I had to keep on telling myself that it was only a temporary thing and that I would soon get the use of my hands and fingers back again.

After the usual hustle and bustle of the early mornings where everything seemed to be happening at the same time, there would be a very quiet time in the ward when all the radios were switched off while Dr Silver did his rounds. It would be about this time that one of the nurses would bring the mail round and more often than not there would be a letter for me. I liked receiving letters or postcards as this made me feel that I hadn't been forgotten. During those early weeks, I think Kate must have got through about two or three note pads as there would be a letter from her nearly every day. The things she found to write about still amaze me. I would also get a letter nearly every week from Jane, my mate Kim's girlfriend. She would tell me all about what was happening down at The Grange. When I was first in hospital and I received a letter I had to ask someone if they would mind reading it to me, but after a month if they took the pages out of the envelope I could manage to hold them with the palms of my hands. This gave me that bit of privacy that we all enjoy when reading a letter. I was also able to use the phone and Mum and Dad or Kate would ring me every other day as we had to share the mobile phone with Ward Two which was just across the corridor. This also gave me another link with the outside world.

As I moved further down the ward there were new cases entering nearly every week, all having damaged spinal cords at various levels. Having asked Jane so many questions I had become an authority on spinal injuries: apparently if you sever your spinal cord completely, from the point of severance down you lose all use and feeling; but if you're what they call 'an incomplete lesion' it means that either your spinal cord is only slightly damaged or it is just suffering from shock — in which case there is a strong possibility that you will get some or all the use back into your body again. I was what they called a 'C6 incomplete lesion'. I had damaged the sixth vertebra from the top of my spine but had not severed it completely, so this gave me hope that I would get the use back into all my body again. Unfortunately there were others in the ward who were not so lucky as I was.

Chapter 5
New Friends, Old Friends

I don't know quite how it came about but on one particular day I heard someone calling out my name. 'Andy.' It must be some other Andy, I thought. Then whoever it was shouted again, so I answered, 'Someone calling me?'

'Hi! My name's Peter, I'm a couple of beds down from you. Your mum was talking to the wife yesterday, so I thought I'd give you a shout to see how you're feeling.'

'Oh, not so bad thanks,' I replied. He carried on the conversation and told me about how he was in Germany and had been knocked down by a lorry and had broken his back. As he talked I tried to put a face to the voice: it was very strange to talk to someone whom you had never seen. We carried on shouting to one another, telling each other all about our injuries and how the accidents happened. Then a voice from the opposite side of the ward joined in: 'Hey, Andy, how long have you been in here?'

'Who's that?' I shouted back.

'My name's Frank. I came in a couple of days ago. I put my lorry into a ditch and have done my back in.' He carried on talking, telling me where he lived, although I could tell by his accent that he was a Londoner. 'Yer, I live at Dagenham near where the big Ford works is.'

'Oh, yer! I know where you mean. I work for the main Ford dealers in my local town.'

We carried on shouting across to one another and I eventually got round to telling him that I had been at Stoke Mandeville for over a month. I asked him who were in the beds on either side of him.

'Oh, on my left there's Kenny. He is from Newcastle and there's Terry on my right — he only came in yesterday.'

I was later to find out that Kenny was in an army truck when it rolled off the road and he consequently had broken his neck very high up. At the beginning he had needed a life support machine to keep him alive and so found it very hard to talk, but although he had lost the feeling in all his body I was to find over the coming weeks that he had not lost his sense of humour.

It was several days later that Terry joined in our now daily chats, and then I found out that he too had broken his neck at the same place as mine. He had been coming home with a friend from a party when they had rolled their car. When he came to he found that he couldn't move. All of us bar one in that ward were suffering either from a broken back or neck and all had different degrees of movement.

The only one who had neither broken his neck nor his back was Keith. At first Keith didn't want to talk to anyone, but after asking one of the nurses what he had done, I found out that he had been given a lift home from the pub by a friend and their car had turned over. When he reached the hospital the doctors found he had ruptured one of the main arteries to his heart, but by the time they managed to operate, the blood supply through his spinal cord had been reduced so much that he was paralysed in his legs, although the rest of his body was virtually OK.

As the days passed we would keep tabs on each other's improvement and also try and cheer one another up: when you were talking you could tell by the tone of the other person's voice if on that particular day he was feeling a bit low. We also began to share each other's visitors. If I had three or four of my regular visitors, like Mum, Dad, Terry and my brother-in-law, John, to see me and they saw that Frank or Kenny had got no one they would disappear for a while and go and chat to them. It was the same with their visitors; if they saw that I had no one they would come over and introduce themselves, then pull up a chair and start chatting away to me as if they had come specially to visit me and not the other person at all. We all seemed to get on well together although we all came from different backgrounds. I suppose it was because we all had the same goals in front of us — first to stay alive and then to win the greatest prize of all — to walk out of the hospital.

Kate had finished school by July and was able to visit more regularly. Not only would she come up with Mum and Dad on Tuesdays and Sundays, but she would cadge a lift with whoever was coming on the other days. This didn't last long, though, as she had to start work at a hairdressers after two weeks' holiday. Things were looking up. I had made friends with the other lads in the ward and now Kate was coming to see me every day. It was on one of these days, when Kate was seeing how much stronger my arms were getting, that I leant my right elbow on the bed cover and pointed my arm upwards. She took hold of it at the wrist and told me to pull it away from her towards me. I did, and at that point felt a twinge shoot right through my body.

'Pull again, Andy,' she said.

'Hang on, babe, I just felt something go right through me. It was like a bloody electric shock.'

'Are you all right? Maybe we shouldn't have done it,' she said anxiously.

I lay there a minute not saying a word.

'You OK, Andy?'

'Yer, I'm fine, but it didn't half make me feel funny.'

She sat there quietly for a moment and then said, 'I'm just going to the loo.' As she lifted her bag up and laid it on the bed I felt something near my leg.

'Did you just touch my leg, Katie?'

She looked at me. 'Did you feel something, then?' she asked.

'I thought I did but it might have been my imagination.' I lay there, only able to see the ceiling as I was on my back, not on either of my sides.

'Let me touch you and see if you can tell me where,' she said.

'OK, then.'

She moved half-way down the bed. 'What am I touching now?'

'My right knee, now my left,' I replied.

'Let's try your toes.' She began to pull up the covers at the bottom of my bed and eventually found my toes. 'All right. What foot am I touching?'

'My left, now my right. I think my big toe on my right, now my little one,' I replied.

She came up to the top of my bed and as she leant over me she seemed to be laughing and crying at the same time. 'You can feel, babe, you can,' and as she kissed me a tear ran down her cheek onto mine. Although I had closed my own eyes I could not stop the tears from seeping from the corners. But, these were not the tears of the heartache of previous weeks but of unbelievable joy. I know that ours were not the only tears shed that day. When Mum and Dad saw that I could feel they too cried: it was as if all our hopes and prayers were being answered.

The following day when Jane arrived to manipulate my limbs I told her the good news about how I could feel. She in turn told Dr Silver after she had satisfied herself that it was true. When Dr Silver and Dr Bash came to see me on their morning rounds they too checked to make sure that I could really feel. It was a strange type of feeling, not the same as I had known before. I could feel someone touching me but I could not feel any pain or anything like that: it was just like a numb sensation, as if a dentist had given me one of those injections for a filling but instead of my mouth it was all over my body. You know how, when you have had the filling and touch your lip with your tongue or bite your lip, you can feel it but you can't feel the perfect sensation or pain that you would if you had bitten your lip before you had had the injection. I hope this is not confusing you too much! In other words, I could feel someone touching my leg or toes but I did not have the perfect sensation as I did before the accident happened. In my position, though, I wasn't about to start splitting hairs — I knew how lucky I really was to be able to feel anything at all.

I began to feel much better in myself and although there was still no movement in the rest of my body I felt a lot more optimistic. As the shock of the accident began to leave me I became more aware of things and people around me: the nurses and orderlies, through their daily supervision, prevented me from getting bed sores, the doctors kept a check on my blood and water works so I didn't get any complications in those areas as they were killers in themselves. I was now beginning to realise how important it had been for me to be moved from my local hospital to here, where they knew how to cope with whatever problem might arise.

Because I was the one injured and lying in bed with callipers coming out of my head, I never quite realised what an ordeal it was for people coming to see me for the first time. Until one particular day, when my friends, Chris and Terry and their two children, arrived to see me. Jackie was about twelve and Darren was ten, and although their parents had tried to explain to them that I wouldn't look the same as I had last time they had seen me, the shock of seeing me lying there with callipers coming out of my head was too much for young Darren. He only managed to say 'hello' before the colour drained from his face and Terry had to carry him quickly outside before he fainted. Young Darren wasn't the only one to fall under the spell of feeling faint. As different friends came to see me, expecting me to look my old self or to look the same as I had last time they had seen me, they were shocked to see me lying there — my face was drawn, you could count my ribs through my almost transparent skin and my hair was very long and thick with grease, having not been washed since the accident. Some appeared not to notice anything and just sat down and started chatting about all sorts of things: whereas others would unconsciously stare and visibly fidget where they sat, looking around, unable to cope with what they saw.

There was one Wednesday when I knew my brother, Bruce, and his wife, Jackie, would be along to visit me. My brother had come every Wednesday since the accident and Jackie would come with him if she could get time off work. I hadn't seen this much of my brother for some time. It wasn't that we had fallen out or anything like that, it was a lot of different things really. He was ten years older than me and when I was seven he had left home and gone to work as a stable lad for one of the trainers in Newmarket. From then on we only saw one another on the odd weekend when either he came home or we went to visit him for the day. We differed in lots of ways: he was always well dressed and enjoyed reading and playing the guitar, and when he was at home he would spend most of his time at the local riding school and hardly give my parents anything to worry about; whereas I am afraid I felt more comfortable in the tattiest pair of jeans I could find, was always out until the last possible moment and through my teenage years had brought umpteen worries and troubles home to my parents. But for all our differences, the crisis that we were both sharing in our different ways had brought us very close together.

'Hi, mate, how are you?' It was Bruce, with Jackie just behind him.

'OK, thanks. Thought you would come along with him today then, Jackie?' I said.

'I was able to get the day off.'

They sat down and started chatting about this and that,

telling me how pleased they had been to hear about me getting my feeling back.

'That was nearly a week ago now,' I said. It was about two o'clock and I asked if they had eaten at one of the roadside cafés along the way. At about three o'clock Dr Bash came into the ward and up to my bed.

'Hello, Andrew. We've decided to take your callipers out this afternoon. All right?'

I knew that the callipers came out after six weeks but had no idea that it was to be today. I asked whether they were going to take me down to the operating room.

'No, I'll do it here,' Dr Bash said. 'Oh crumbs,' I thought; he is not even going to put me out.' He disappeared for a moment and when he returned he asked if my brother and his wife would mind going for a coffee or down to the other end of the ward for a little while.

He pulled the curtain round my bed and then one of the nurses came over to give him a hand.

'Hey, Dr Bash, this isn't going to hurt, is it?' I asked.

'Oh no, I'll spray this freezing lotion on first so that you won't feel a thing.' He went round to the top end of my bed and began to spray the freezing lotion on each temple where the callipers went in. As I lay there, my stomach began to churn over and over and I began to breathe much more deeply as I got more and more apprehensive about what was about to happen. Then suddenly I felt there was nothing pulling my head back and realised that they must have removed the weights from the callipers.

'OK, then, I'm going to unscrew them a little at a time, first one side and then the other.'

I felt a sudden jar in my skull as Dr Bash put the metal spanner to the metal callipers. As he began to unscrew them I could feel the screws gradually withdrawing from my skull.

'Nurse, they're starting to bleed a little bit, can you get some gauze and tape please?' asked Dr Bash. He carried on loosening them and then suddenly they were out. He was right! I hadn't felt any pain but my temples did seem to feel a little tender. The nurse returned and remarked how much better I looked without the callipers and then proceeded to put a piece of gauze on the two holes where they had been. Then she pulled back the curtains and disappeared up the ward. Bruce and Jackie, noticing the curtains had been pulled back, came over. 'Hey, Andy, I bet you feel better now you've got rid of them, don't you?' Bruce said.

'Yer, I do, mate,' I replied. Then they asked whether it had hurt much and when I told them that I hardly felt a thing I don't think they could quite believe it — mind you, neither could I!

That night when first Mum then Kate rang to see how I was and I told them I had had the callipers removed earlier that day, they were both over the moon and with their different words of encouragement lifted my spirits higher than they had been for some weeks. After they had hung up I was lying in bed quietly when I heard Frank's voice call out, 'Hey, Andy, is that right? You had your callipers out this afternoon.' I shouted back that it was and we carried on talking to one another with the other lads chipping in from time to time.

Our chats in the evenings were a regular thing. We were allowed visitors at any time of the day and they could stop for as long as they wished. Because we came from different parts of the country the hospital authorities realised that our visitors would want to stay as long as possible as they probably wouldn't be able to come as often as if we were in local hospitals. After they had left we would chat to one another until twelve and later, then finally one by one we would drop off to sleep. I think those late night chats were the reason for most of my visitors finding me asleep when they arrived to see me.

When Kate arrived the next day a big smile came over her face when she saw me without my callipers. 'I think I preferred you with them in,' she said jokingly, sitting down and beginning to tell me all her news. I had a feeling she wanted to say something to me but didn't know how to put

39

it. As I listened to her, I was thinking the worst: 'Perhaps she's going to say she wants to finish with me; I can't blame her if she does — it can't be much fun coming up here every week just sitting and looking at the state I'm in. How the hell can she still love me the way I am now?' I was turning all this over in my mind and I knew I had to ask her what was wrong.

'Hey, babe, what's wrong? Is there something you want to tell us? Do you want to finish? I know it can't be much fun coming up here and seeing me the way I am now.'

She looked straight into my eyes and took hold of my hand and said, 'I never want to finish with you, babe, I don't care if you don't get any better, I love you for you and that's all that matters. Anyway, you are going to get better and you're going to walk me up the aisle one day. I thought you might be fed up with me.'

'No, Katie, I will never be fed up with you,' I said. 'I love you with all my heart, and without you coming to see me I don't think I could have got through one week let alone these last six.'

She squeezed my hand and we both peered into each other's eyes. I don't know who said it, but one of us suggested that we should get engaged.

'Let's make it my birthday,' Kate said. It would be in just two weeks' time, on 30th June. After Kate had gone I lay there pondering whether she had agreed to getting engaged out of pity for me. Over the time we had been going out with one another there had been other things which had gone wrong, but together we had managed to overcome them. So was it out of pity or was it because she loved me — only time would tell I told myself.

That Saturday some of my mates from The Grange came to see me. As they walked toward my bed I noticed Gary was carrying a box.

'Hello, Andy!' he said. 'We've bought you a present from all the lads. We've been collecting money for you since your accident and have put it all together to buy you this. It's what your mum said you would like.' As he turned the box round I could see a picture of a radio cassette recorder.

'Oh great, thank all the people who gave money towards it for me, won't you? It's ever so kind of them.' Inside I was really chuffed to think that the lads had given some of their hard earned cash to buy me this lovely present. Gary plugged it in and then stood it on my bedside cabinet. It sounded really good and I told them that I could now play my favourite tapes.

My mates from The Grange had been really good to me since the accident happened — not only buying me this radio, but they frequently came to visit me. I remembered that only a weekend earlier about three car loads of them had arrived to see me and had had to take it in turns to come in the ward. There was one of them who came up more than the others, though. That was my old mate, Terry. We had been friends a long time now, from playing football on the local playing field to going through secondary school and so on. Although he was a couple of years older than I was this had never seemed to matter. Mind you, most of my mates were either one or two years older than myself. One of my best memories of an evening with Terry was when he was going out with a girl called Lucy. She had just packed him in for another bloke and he was feeling pretty miserable, so when he heard she was going to be at a disco we were going to, he decided to get a little the worse for wear — that's a bit of an understatement. Anyway, we never managed even to get to the disco! After drinking almost a full bottle of wine on his own, we spent the rest of the night walking him round the local housing estate, stopping at every appropriate drain so that he could throw up. After that I had to get him home on his bike and remind him that he had to pedal a bike to make it move. We eventually got home after a couple of somersaults onto the bank at the side of the road. But the biggest laugh occurred the following morning. When Terry was drunk, we had arranged to go pea picking the next day at seven o'clock in the morning. So there I stood, knocking on his back door. His dad stuck his head out of the bedroom window, and I asked whether Terry was coming pea picking. His dad said that he hadn't come home last night at all. At that moment the door of the garden shed opened and who should appear but Terry! He hadn't been able to make anybody hear the night before and so he'd had to sleep on the bench in the shed. We still went pea picking, but had to come away just after lunch as Terry was still feeling the effects of the night before. Although I recall this memory, many a time the shoe was on the other foot, so to speak.

Chapter 6
One Good Day but a Bad Week

By the middle of June the days were getting warmer, and every morning I would be awakened by the sun shining through the window directly behind my bed. Although I enjoyed this at first, as the day drew on the strong sunshine would tend to push my temperature sky high. So I, and the rest of the lads in bed, had to have fans beside our beds to blow air over us to keep us as cool as possible. If this was not enough the nurses would put cold flannels on our foreheads, as there was a big risk in our temperature going too high. Not only did we have to cope with the heat, there was another problem. One morning, when the nurses were giving me my bed bath, one of them noticed that I had a slight pressure sore on my bottom. After the doctor had seen it he told the orderlies only to turn me from side to side, and not to give me any time on my back. This meant that I got no relief from the chin pad that I wrote about earlier. Now the callipers were out I hoped I would not need the pad for much longer. My neck was getting much stronger and I was able to move my head without going dizzy. My hopes were fulfilled the following morning when Sister Shilton said that I could remove it. The relief was beyond belief, but it took some time for the soreness to leave my jaw and I still felt a tenderness for many days afterwards.

The day after my chin pad was removed Jane arrived as usual to manipulate my limbs.

'Hey, Jane, when will I be getting out of bed, do you think?'

She carried on stretching my fingers out straight and then bending them into a fist. 'You have still got some time to go before you can start getting up, Andy.'

I paused for a moment. 'Well, how long do you think?' I asked again.

'Let's see,' she said. 'It's been just over six weeks and your callipers have been out a few days. If you really want to know, Andy, you've got to stay in bed for at least another five to six weeks, I'm afraid.'

'Another five weeks! You're joking!' But when I looked at her face I could see that she wasn't. 'The trouble is, although I still get plenty of visitors and you come to see me twice a day, I'm getting really bored in the times between.'

She had now moved onto my other hand. 'Why don't you try reading a book or something?' she suggested.

'I can hardly hold a letter, Jane, let alone a book,' I replied.

'I'll get in touch with the Occupational Therapy department,' she said. 'I'm sure they can fix you up with one of their stands. They stretch across the bed and hold the book for you.' She then moved down my legs as usual.

'What happens when I get out of bed, Jane? What about therapy then?' I asked.

'There are two therapy departments; one just a short distance up the corridor, past the canteen you've heard your mum and dad talk about.'

She then went on to tell me about the different things that happened in the different departments. 'In Occupational Therapy they teach you to dress and wash your hair and type and hold a knife and fork and so on.' As she told me about the different things that went on, the words were going in but not really registering. I was still in the frame of mind that believed I would not need this help by the time I got out of bed: the strength in my muscles and limbs would have returned. I let her carry on talking about the other things that I would be doing once I got out of bed, such as swimming and doing archery. 'Um, archery. Hey, that sounds good,' I thought to myself. Jane finished off my legs and then left to visit one of her many other patients.

That afternoon one of the occupational therapists arrived with the book stand. She placed a book on it, then fastened it down. She then placed a stick with a rubber thimble on the end in the strap which I used for feeding myself: this was to enable me to turn the pages. I would have to flick one of the pages out from under the elastic band on one side and tuck it under another on the other side. The only trouble was that instead of one page coming out at a time, there would usually be half a dozen or more. As I began to read I started to feel dizzy and had to close my eyes to stop the swimming sensation in my head. I persevered with the reading but as I had never been a person to read before my accident, and as it had now been made that much harder, I soon grew bored with it and decided I would have another go next day.

Mum and Dad arrived that afternoon and sensed immediately that I was a bit uptight from not being able to do a simple thing like read a book. They chatted to me as usual and tried to bring out the pent-up emotion that I felt. After a little while Dad made an excuse to disappear and seemed to be gone some time. He eventually returned carrying a large square box. 'I went and asked sister if it would be all right to buy you a telly now that you've had your callipers out. She said it was so I went down to the town and got it right away.' Most of the lads in bed who had recovered from the initial shock had got a portable TV on their bedside cabinets, as it was almost impossible to see the picture on the main one at the bottom of the ward. Dad unpacked it and set it up for me beside my bed. 'At least I can watch some of my favourite programmes and there is Wimbledon starting soon,' I thought to myself. But I hadn't realised that concentrating on the picture would have the same effect as reading the book had had, and my head was soon spinning as before. As the days passed and I watched more and more TV the dizziness subsided and only occurred occasionally.

Kate and I had to bring the engagement forward two days as the thirtieth fell on a Wednesday and Kate would have started her job at the hairdressers by then. The day arrived and both Kate's parents and mine came up to share the occasion with us. Mum had had a special engagement cake made at the local bakers and Kate had chosen and bought both rings. They all stood round my bed and we slipped the rings on each other's fingers. As I had lost quite a bit of weight since my accident the ring slipped off my finger, so a piece of sticky tape was applied. Then came the task of cutting the cake. As I could not grip, Kate first curled my fingers round the handle of the knife and then with her hand over mine gripped for both of us and, with all her strength, cut into the cake. Mum then cut it all up and handed it to everyone in the ward — which was greeted with shouts of congratulations from the lads in bed. Kate opened the cards and presents that people had been kind enough to send us. There were cards from the different members of both our families and from some of our friends back home. Kate told me about the presents that we had received: there was a small lamp and a tray with some glasses and many other things. The time had slipped by and it was getting very near the time when Kate and my parents would have to be making a move for home. Over the last couple of weeks I had been able to control my emotions when it was time for my regular visitors to leave but today it was different. I managed to say goodbye to Kate's parents, but as I said goodbye to my own mum and dad a lump was beginning to come up into my throat. Now it was time to say goodbye to Kate, knowing also that from now on I would only see her on Sundays — and on Mondays as that was her day off. After having seen her almost every day for the last couple of weeks this was going to be hard enough, without the fact that I was about to say goodbye on the day we had just got engaged.

Kate spoke first. 'I don't want to go, babe, but starting work tomorrow and everything, I've got no choice. I'll write to you every day and phone in the evenings and I will be back to see you again on Sunday.' She was trying to justify her leaving to herself as much as to me.

'Hey, that's OK, babe, I understand.' I had said the words without realising that I had done so. She leant over me and gave me a long kiss. I put my arm round her neck in an attempt to hold onto her but I knew I had to let her go. As she walked away she turned and looked. I forced a smile onto my face and then she was gone.

I tried to focus on the ceiling but my eyes were quickly filling with tears. 'Oh lord, help me, please,' I said in nothing more than a whisper so no one would hear me saying it. I was alone and not even watching the television or listening to the radio could take away the dreadful feeling of loneliness.

I had no visitors the following day and just lay there listening to several of my favourite tapes and trying to move my fingers by squeezing a ball that Mum had bought in for me the previous day. I had another go at reading my book but soon asked the nurse if she would mind moving it away as I couldn't turn the pages over correctly and it was only causing me to sink deeper into the depths of depression.

It was late into the afternoon when Frank called over. 'Hey, Andy. Anything wrong? Haven't heard from you all day. Are you all right?'

'Yer, I'm all right, thanks,' I replied. 'I just haven't got a lot to say for myself. I suppose if I tell the truth, after getting engaged yesterday, today seems a bit of an anticlimax.'

He shouted over a few more times but must have realised that I wasn't in the mood for chatting and so stopped.

After the evening meal was over, Mum rang me. As I listened to her loving voice at the other end the feeling of wanting to jump out of bed and run all the way home came flashing into my mind. It seemed most of my family were at home that evening and the phone was passed from one to the other. After Mum, came Dad, then Jo and finally Lou and then it was passed back to Mum to have the last word. No sooner had the nurse put back the receiver when it was ringing again. 'It's for you again, Andy,' the nurse said. It was Kate this time and she told me all about her first day at work and how she had been writing me a letter before she decided to ring me. We carried on talking until we couldn't think of anything else to say, then finally told each other how much we loved one another and then she was gone.

The following day I had some good news. The pressure sores had gone from my bottom which meant I could lie on my back again. Bruce arrived as usual, as it was Wednesday, and as we sat chatting who should come round the corner but my old mate, Brynly.

'Hello, Andy. How are you, mate?' he said. Brynly had been up once before but as he was in the army he could not visit as often as some of my other mates.

'I'm not too bad, thanks, mate. I didn't now you were coming. How did you get up here?' I asked.

'I caught the train to Liverpool Street and then got the train to Aylesbury and here I am.' He sat down and told me what he had been up to in the army, about the assault courses he had to go on and about the driving test he had taken and passed in one of the army trucks. I told him about the physiotherapy I was receiving now and how my arms were improving and the fact that I could feel my body again.

'Oh great, mate,' he said and I could see by his face that he was pleased with the news.

All three of us carried on talking most of the afternoon, only being interrupted by the orderlies who came to turn me every two hours. Between them they had lifted me out of my depression. Around six o'clock Brynly said he would have to make a move so he didn't miss his train. My brother offered him a lift to the station and they left. Bruce returned and stopped for another hour or so and then he also had to make a move for home. We said our goodbyes and he promised to come again next Wednesday.

I had felt warm most of the day, and just put it down to the warm weather that we were having. But now that both Bruce and Brynly had left I started to feel quite sick. I tried to put the thought of being sick out of my mind but it was no good, and when I began to bring up my tea I knew I must be sick. The trouble was I was on my back and unable to sit up, I began to choke on the very stuff I was trying to get rid of. The old boy, Les, who was in the next bed must have seen me choking as I heard him shout out. 'Nurse, quick! Andy's being sick!' The nurse came running over to me and pressed the button on my bed so it tilted me onto my side. Then another nurse arrived with a stainless steel bowl for me to be sick in rather than all over my sheets. For those few seconds I panicked, trying to be sick then having to swallow it again as there was no way I could get it out of my mouth. I lay there listening to my heart seemingly pounding ten times faster than usual. I brought my tea up again, but this time I was able to get rid of it into the bowl. I closed my eyes and felt as if I was burning up, the sweat was running off my forehead. One of the nurses must have called a doctor as within minutes Dr Bash was beside me.

'OK, Andy, I'm just going to take your blood pressure,' he said and began to wrap this thing round my arm.

'What's wrong with me, doc? I feel as if I'm burning a hole where I lie,' I said.

He carried on taking my blood pressure. 'Oh there is nothing to worry about; I think you've got a water infection,' he answered. 'Don't worry, I will soon have it under control.'

This is how you feel when you have a water infection then, is it? I had heard the other lads say how ill they had felt when they had had one and I knew what was to come. Dr Bash then took blood and urine samples which were sent off for analysis. Then he stuck a needle into one of the main veins in my left arm and a stand was brought to the side of my bed. A bag of clear liquid was hung from it and a tube from the bag connected to the needle. There was a small device at the bottom of the bag where I could see a constant drip drop down and then through into the tube. Then he gave me some pills to take and finally he left.

I did not sleep much that night and when morning came I still did not feel too good. Breakfast arrived and I was informed that I wasn't allowed any — not that I felt like it anyway. Then came doctors' rounds and Dr Bash described what had happened the day before and what he had done and prescribed to cure it. Dr Silver had a close look at the bag of urine that hung from the side of my bed and told the sister to put me on a different course of pills. As I was already taking between twenty and twenty-five pills a day for different reasons a few more wouldn't make any difference, I thought.

Mum was due that day and didn't know anything about what had happened the evening before. In addition, she was bringing some old family friends who had not been to visit me before. As Mum walked into the ward with the people who I call my Aunty Lil and Uncle Stan she passed right by my bed. Then I saw her stop the sister and ask her if I had been moved. I could see the sister explaining what had happened and then they came over to where I lay.

'Hello, dear, the sister said you have had a bad time.'

I could see that my mum's face had lost all its colour and that she was struggling to put her words together. 'They tell me I've got a water infection.' I saw her glance quickly at the stand beside my bed·and then back to me lying there in bed. Whatever little bit of colour that had returned to my face had now disappeared again.

Mum took hold of my hand. 'I was only telling Stan and Lillian how much better you were,' she said.

I looked at them both and tried to smile to make them more at ease. I wanted to talk to them, ask them about their journey up here, but this water infection had taken almost every last drop of energy that I had left. I think they must have realised this as they only answered my questions and did not carry on the conversation. The rest of the time they sat quietly beside my bed and only spoke now and again. Aunty Lil and Uncle Stan made an excuse to go down to the canteen for a cup of tea to give Mum and me some time alone.

After they had gone Mum started to cry. 'I was expecting you to look so well. I'd been telling them all the way up here how much better you were,' she blurted out as she cried and tried to blow her nose at the same time.

'Hey, Mum, I'm going to be all right. It's only a water infection. It will be gone in a couple of days! Anyway, you're the one who's meant to be cheering me up, not me cheering you!'

This brought a small smile to her face. It was the first time I had seen Mum cry since the accident had happened, although I knew she must have shed bucket loads. I think the cry must have done her some good as after that she seemed to brighten up and began to tell me what was happening at home. Then Aunty Lillian and Uncle Stan returned and told me all about their family and what they were all doing with themselves. Time had drawn on and I knew Mum was reluctant to leave me but she knew she must. I tried to apologise for not being very good company after they had travelled all that way to visit me, but they said they understood and that they hoped I would soon feel better. Mum rang me that night when she got home to see if I was feeling any better and I told her that I was. I did feel better and that night slept quite well. Two days later the drip was taken out of my arm and I was allowed to eat and drink again, but I don't think I had ever felt that ill before in my life.

Chapter 7
No More Itching

In July I began receiving post-cards nearly every day from the different friends who were on their holidays. My sister, Brenda, was one for the post-cards. She had been sending a card from her and the children every week since the accident had happened. The pictures were mainly of East Bergholt and the surrounding countryside — very popular with tourists, so you could buy the post-cards in almost all the little shops in the village. Looking at the cards gave me a kind of link with home and many happy memories would come flooding back into my mind. My memories were always of a particular place or a certain girl who I had been there with. Although Kate and I had been going out with one another for a long time we had split up several times, and this had given me the chance to go out with other girls. I am not saying that I was — or that I am — Mr Tall, Dark and Handsome and that all I had to do was whistle and they would come running, but I always seemed to manage to get on well with the opposite sex. You see, the trouble with blokes is that all they want to tell you is who they had and when they had her. I could never see the point in bragging about different girls that I had had; it only made the girl look cheap when really you had been the lucky one — lucky enough to find yourself in the company of a really nice girl with the opportunity of doing more than just kissing one another. I've got many great memories that only the girl and I know about, but looking back I wish that I had had a much longer and lasting relationship with a couple of the girls that I went out with in my teenage years. They will no doubt know who I'm talking about if the day ever comes when they read this. The Lord knew what he was doing when he decided to set aside a piece of our brain for a memory bank, because without memories to call upon my many weeks in bed would have been unbearable.

I had now been in bed for two and a half months and my hair had grown very long and become horribly greasy; added to this my scalp was driving me mad from the constant itching that came from not having had it washed for so long. I knew it was impossible to have it washed while the callipers were in, but they had been removed over four weeks ago and the places where they had fitted onto my temples had healed up quite well, so I asked one of the nurses if it was possible to have my hair washed while I was still in bed.

'Oh yes,' she said. 'If I get time this afternoon I'll do it for you.'

'Great!' I thought, 'perhaps then I won't look as if I've got nits, constantly scratching my head.'

There were no visitors on this particular day so it gave an ideal opportunity. Marcia came back to me after lunch. 'OK, Andy, are you ready to have your hair washed, then?' She was a young nurse, only about nineteen, black, and with a tight affro hairdo.

'Yer, great! I can't wait!' I replied.

She disappeared and returned with a large sheet of plastic and a couple of bowls which she put on the floor; then she began to wash my hair. Oh it felt great: the warm water and the way she gently massaged my head! She rinsed the soap out and then dried it off with a hair drier. Just a simple thing like having my hair washed gave me a reassuring feeling that I was well on the road to recovery. Marcia came round to the side of my bed and took a long look at my hair. 'I must say, it's a big improvement,' she said, with an admiring smile on her face. I smiled back knowing that she was just having some fun with me. She was a really nice girl. We both liked Motown music and over the last few weeks had begun borrowing each other's tapes, which had resulted in our forming a friendship of more than just the nurse and patient kind.

When Mum rang that night she told me that she and Dad would be on holiday next week. 'But don't worry,' she said. 'We've decided to find a place that does bed and breakfast near the hospital. That way we can take Lou out during the day and in the evenings we can come to the hospital to see you.' 'That's great,' I thought, 'a whole week of seeing them every night.'

And that is what they did. They found a small pub not far from the hospital, took Lou to different local attractions during the day, such as the wild life park and seeing the sights in Aylesbury; then they would arrive at the hospital around six o'clock and spend the whole of the evening with me, telling me what they had been doing during the day.

I realise now that it couldn't have been much of a holiday for them, especially for Lou. It must have been really boring for her to spend the evenings just sitting beside my bed and there wasn't really an awful lot to do during the day as Aylesbury wasn't noted for its tourist attractions; but from my point of view it was really great to have them there with me every evening. As the week drew to a close, I wondered how I would cope when their holiday was over.

On Sunday, Kate arrived as usual. 'Hey, Andy, I've got some great news! You know my sister Sue's husband, Paul? Well, his mum and dad live only about eight miles away from here and they have said I can stop there Sunday nights, so that means I can spend all day Monday with you.' This news was like music to my ears and made saying goodbye to Mum, Dad and Lou much easier. As Mum and Dad left they promised to be up sometime the following week. I seemed to be in two frames of mind: on one hand, pleased with the news Kate had greeted me with and on the other, sad at having to say goodbye to my parents and young sister.

Kate now arrived first thing in the mornings on her visiting days and sat with me all through the day until whoever was taking her home that night decided to make a move. It was great to have her there all that time, although sometimes the conversation would run dry between us. Then we would think about — and later tell each other — what great things we were going to do once I got out of hospital. Oh, there was so much that we wanted to do together, like going on holidays abroad and getting our own place — a little flat in town just like our friends Della and David. They were just dreams in the sky, but the thing was would we be able to reach them one day?

Chapter 8
Right, Andy.
How would you like to sit up?

The start of yet another new day and as I lay in bed I could hear the doctors starting their rounds. I had been in the ward for almost ten weeks now so was no longer the first in the queue. 'Hello, how are you this morning?' I heard Dr Silver say as he moved on to the next bed. Then he went on to discuss a particular problem with the other members of his band of merry men. Me next. 'Hello, Andrew, how are you this morning?'

'Oh I'm not too bad thanks,' I replied.

'Let's have a look at his notes, please, sister. You've been in bed nearly ten weeks, then. I suppose we had better think about getting you up soon. He has still got a catheter in, I see, it's about time we tried him without it. I would also like him to have an IVP done sometime this week and we had better take some more X-Rays to see how well his neck has healed. And, Dr Bash, perhaps you can take some measurements so we can order a wheelchair for him?'

'Dr Silver's really going to town this morning,' I thought to myself after they had moved over to the other side of the ward. I called Marcia over, 'Dr Silver says I can have my catheter out and he said something about having an IVP done, whatever one of those is.' I knew that having the catheter out was good news, because now I would have to learn how to pass my water on my own rather than have this tube pushed down my penis and into my bladder. 'But what on earth's an IVP?' I asked Marcia again.

'Well, you have to go down to the X-Ray department and there a doctor will come and inject you with a syringe of dye so that when they X-Ray you they'll be able to see your bladder and kidneys. Then they can tell if they are working OK. They'll probably take the X-Rays of your neck at the same time,' she said.

After the doctors' rounds had finished Dr Bash returned and asked lots of questions so he could order me a wheelchair. 'How much did you weigh before your accident? How tall are you?' He jotted down pages of notes and then left. After he had gone I lay there thinking about what Dr Silver had said. Ten weeks ago I had taken each day as it came, not giving much thought to what was going to happen. Now, here I was, after ten weeks in bed, being measured up for a wheelchair and told I'd soon be getting up and using it. I should have been pleased but, in truth, I hated the very thought of being in a wheelchair. I'd been telling myself for weeks that by the time I got out of bed my muscles and limbs would be working for me again and I wouldn't need a chair to get around in. All the time I remained in bed, that is what I could believe; but now, in a few days' time, I was going to have to face up to reality. Instead of being pleased with the thought of finally getting up, I was bloody depressed. But then, what were the alternatives? Either I could stay in bed for the rest of my life, or get up into that chair and then fight like hell to get out of it.

I was turning this over in my mind when Lawrence, one of the orderlies, came to my bed and pulled the curtains round it. I knew he was about to take the catheter out. Although I was pleased, it was at times like this that I felt most humiliated. The accident wouldn't have been quite so bad if I had been able to do the two most personal things that I had always taken for granted, but which I now needed help with every day: if I could get back the use of my bladder and bowels, then and only then would I be able to have my self-dignity returned. Lawrence removed the catheter and placed a bottle between my legs. Then he left.

'Hey, Andy, I hear you're being measured up for an S registration!' It was Frank: he must have heard Dr Bash taking my measurements.

'Yer, I've got one of the new models coming; only trouble is this garage is a bit slow on delivery.'

Frank joked that everybody would keep well away from Ward Two once I got my new set of wheels. Although I was pleased to be getting to the point where I would soon be getting up and around in a wheelchair, I had hoped that by this time my limbs and muscles would have been working again. Now I had to convince myself that they would start to work again once I began the physiotherapy that I could get from the different departments in the hospital.

I soon discerned that I could pass my water naturally, although I did not have any real control over my bladder muscles: in other words, I could not stop and start whenever I wanted to, but when my bladder was full I would pass some — mind you, I was lucky, because I could feel when I wanted to go and this would become a great help in the future.

On the same day the catheter was taken away I had my IVP done. They wheeled me down to the X-Ray department and then Dr Bash came in. 'Hello, Andrew. What I'm going to do is inject this dye into your arm. If you feel a warm feeling in the back of your throat just say and I will go a bit slower, but don't try and spit it out, just swallow, please.'

I watched him fix the syringe and I'm telling you it was bloody huge! 'He's never going to pump all that into me, is he?' I thought, but unfortunately he was. He stuck the needle into my arm then began slowly to pump the dye into me; my eyes began to water and then I felt the burning sensation in the back of my throat that he had warned me about, so I swallowed several times as he carried on. Then it was over and he removed the large syringe.

'OK. Lie there a minute so the dye can get through your system and then someone will come and take some X-Rays of you.'

I lay there looking up at the ceiling until the radiographer came into the room.

'Hi, I'm just going to take a few X-Rays, OK?' she said, then she began to move the apparatus into the correct positions over my body. After this it was a case of 'Breathe in. Now hold it. Now let it out,' then the equipment was moved to another position and the same instructions on how to breathe were given to me again. Then it was over and the orderlies returned to push me back to the ward.

It was now late into the afternoon and as I hadn't been allowed anything to eat since breakfast I was starving. They pushed my bed back into the space where it had come from, then one of the Auxiliary nurses came over.

'How would you like egg on toast?'

'Oh that would be great if I could, please,' and with that she left to go and prepare it.

I heard one of the lads shout out: 'It's all right for some, getting egg on toast in the afternoon when all we've got is bread and jam!'

It was a regular thing in the afternoons for a trolley to be brought round with an urn of tea, bread, butter and an assortment of jams for everyone in the ward. Even those in wheelchairs would return to the ward for their afternoon tea. I soon polished off my egg and a couple of cups of tea. 'I'll be glad when I don't have to drink my tea through a straw,' I told myself, 'but I think I'll be able to last out now until the evening meal is brought round.'

Later on that afternoon Dr Bash came over to see me. 'The X-Rays are OK and I think you will be changing from this bed into another one which will enable you to sit up gradually. You see, you must get back your sense of gravity before we put you into a wheelchair.'

That night, on the telephone, I told my parents and then Kate what had happened that day; the X-Rays, then the good news about changing beds. I could tell by their reaction on the other end of the phone that they were very pleased with the news I had just told them. That night, as I lay there in the darkness of the ward, I kept asking myself the same questions: once I get in a wheelchair and start doing proper therapy, will I get back the use of my muscles and limbs? 'Again. Oh, dear Lord, I ask you with all my heart, please let this be true,' I kept saying to myself until I must have finally dropped off to sleep.

Early on the following day things began to happen. 'OK, Andy, after we've given you your bath we'll change the beds over.' It was Sister Shilton who was doing the talking. They finished washing me as usual and then called the orderlies to lift me so the pillows could be puffed up. But this time, instead of just puffing up the pillows, they removed the whole bed and put my new bed in its place. No longer would a simple push of a button turn me onto my side. I now had to be lifted and turned as the new bed's mechanism would only tilt the bed upwards and not from side to side. By the time the changeover was finished it was lunch, and the other lads who were up and about had all disappeared to their different courses of therapy. I saw Sister Shilton coming towards me. 'Right, Andy. How would you like to sit up a fraction?'

The old butterflies began to flutter in my stomach. 'I would like to very much, please.'

She pressed a button down beside my bed, only allowing the bed to tilt up a few degrees. 'How's that?' she asked.

I was high enough to be able to look straight across the other side of the ward and could at last put a face to some of the familiar voices that I had regularly heard over the last few weeks. Then, suddenly, I began to feel a bit light headed, and I told sister, who was still standing beside me.

'Don't worry!' she said. 'Everyone feels like that when they progress from lying flat to sitting up. Just take some deep breaths.' I did as she said and the dizziness began to fade away.

I could just see Frank, lying there on the opposite side of the ward, so I called out to him, 'Hey, Frank, I can see your ugly face at last!'

I was only joking with him, but he did have a couple of large cuts on his face where he had gone through the windscreen of his lorry. As he turned towards me I noticed he had much more movement than I did as he had damaged only the lower part of his spine.

'Hello, Andy,' he said in his London accent, as he lifted himself onto his elbow. 'Talk about me being ugly, you haven't looked at yourself in the mirror for quite a while, I take it,' and we both grinned at one another.

Beside him was Peter who had injured his spinal cord at roughly the same place as me but, unlike me, he had decided to have his hair shaved off before they put the callipers in. Although they were out now, his hair was still very short. He lay there, flat on his back, looking very pale and thin. 'I wonder if I look like that,' I thought to myself.

On the other side of Frank was Kenny. With no disrespect, he looked worse than Peter: he had dark brown hair and I noticed a large red mark on his throat; this, I later found out, was where he had had a tube put in to enable him to breathe. He was in the same position as me with his bed also tilted up, but as he had been in longer than I had, he was that little bit higher. I let my eyes take in all that they could without daring to move my head, thinking that if I did I would break my neck again. I noticed that Max, one of the new patients, had got some visitors with him, and I also saw for the first time the large jugs of water on each of the lads' lockers, plus numerous other things such as radios, portable tellies and little mascots or good luck charms hanging from the handles of their drawers. Sister Shilton left me for a short while, then came back. 'OK, Andy, I think that's enough for one day. Tomorrow we will let you go a little bit higher.' She pressed the button and gently lowered me down to the horizontal position and to my familiar view of the ceiling. Although I had only been raised a few degrees and for only just about ten or fifteen minutes I really felt good about my improvement.

Over the next couple of days my bed was raised that bit more each time and I even got brave enough to turn my head a little bit so I could see the top end of the ward where I had been to start with. There they were, the newly-arrived and very ill men and young lads, their families sitting very close to their beds, talking and trying to comfort them as best they could. Turning my head to the left, I could see down to the bottom end of the ward: the telly on its high stand had been getting more visible as I had moved further down the ward but now I saw the empty beds of the lads who were up and around and the two large green tables with various vases of flowers where they sat to eat their meals. I watched the nurses and the orderlies going about their business, first seeing to someone at one end of the ward and then hurrying to another patient at the other end. Although most people at the far end were up and around, there was the odd lad who had had to go back to bed with a minor complication. I watched the orderlies pull the curtains round the different people in bed and listened to the groans as they were turned or tended to in some way. Frank was improving greatly and I watched as his physiotherapist put him through his paces. He now had some strength in his right leg and she seemed to be concentrating on this. She pulled the covers off and laid a sand bag over his leg, at the bottom of his shin between his leg and his foot. As she had a couple of pillows under his knee joint this meant his leg was bent. He found straightening his leg from this position quite easy, so she put a sand bag over his foot to make things that bit harder. As he lay in bed, Frank had to use his muscles that much more and he was getting stronger without even getting up.

Oh how I wished I could do the same. I suppose it was a bit like trying to diet and having someone sit right in front of you eating a fresh cream cake. I could not say anything about the way I felt, either, as they would have thought I was envious and jealous-minded. They would have been right, and so would you if you think the same thing. I was deadly jealous of people who were further on than I was.

Jane came down the ward towards me. 'You're not sitting up again, are you?' she said as she reached my bed. I had been allowed to sit up a little while for the past three days and I was starting to get used to the dizziness that came over me every time my bed was raised. Jane was still coming twice a day to manipulate my limbs and as she worked on my hands she told me that I would probably be getting out of bed sometime next week, as long as there weren't any problems between now and then. It was now Friday. I knew Mum and Dad were coming up to see me and it would be the first time they had seen me sitting up in bed. It would be great to see them come into the ward, instead of listening to footsteps and wondering if that was them.

It was great. As they reached my bed I could see the joy on their faces. Although I had told them the news on the phone, they were so happy to actually see it with their own eyes. After they had been with me for quite some time the sister came over to my bed. 'Hello, Mr and Mrs Tricker,' she said. 'I wonder, Mrs Tricker, could you bring some of Andy's clothes in when you next come; and could you buy him a pair of training shoes, preferably a size bigger than he usually takes. He will be starting to get up in the next few days.'

Mum agreed at once and Sister left. Mum and Dad were over the moon. 'That's great, isn't it, Andy? I'll send your clothes up with Jo and Tim tomorrow, OK?'

I knew it wasn't going to be long before I was allowed out of bed but as it drew closer I got more and more apprehensive about it. You see, while I was in this bed I was safe, there was no danger. I was in my own little world where I could dream away the day, imagining I was completely well, able to walk and do all the other things that had been taken away from me. But once I got out of bed, then I would have to face reality. Mum and Dad left that evening much happier than usual, knowing that when they returned in the middle of the following week I would be up and about in my wheelchair.

Chapter 9
Up and About

Saturday had been and gone. I had had some of my mates from the garage to visit me. There was Les, Noddy, Fritz and another lad. They had spent most of the afternoon with me except when they went for a bite to eat in the local town of Aylesbury. It was really good to see them and they told me what had been happening at work and how my mate, Andy, (who had started at the same time as I) had also had an accident on his motorbike and had broken both his arms. 'You ought to see him, Andy, he has got plaster from his wrists to his shoulders,' Fritz said and then they all had a good laugh. It was really great to see them and to catch up on all that had been happening at work. I was lying there thinking about what they had talked about and had a laugh to myself about what they had said. I must have then fallen off to sleep as the next thing I knew was that the orderlies were about to turn me. It was strange, really, how I'd got used to being turned all through the night. I would wake from my sleep while they turned me but as soon as they had gone I would go back into a deep sleep again.

On the Sunday afternoon after Sister Shilton asked Mum to bring my clothes I was sitting up again when Jo, Tim and Kate arrived. They all said how pleased they were to see me sitting up. I could see Jo carrying a small case as she came towards my bed.

'Come to take me home have you, Jo?' I said.

'I wish I could, Andy.' There was only a couple of years between me and Jo and for that reason we seemed to be very close, although there were times when we didn't see eye to eye, so to speak, and had our rows like any other brother and sister. As I had been sitting up for quite some time the orderlies came over to lower me and turn me at the same time. They always made sure I was turned onto my side after sitting up as there was always the danger of getting a pressure sore. I told Tim that I'd got to get a pair of trainers.

'What do you think of these?' he said as he lifted his foot onto my bed.

'Yer, I wouldn't mind a pair of those,' I said, so he offered to go into Aylesbury and get me a pair.

Jo and Tim left and so gave me and Kate some time on our own. She told me all about what she had been up to during the week. At first, after my accident, she hadn't gone out of the door but now she was going out more and more. Although I knew she couldn't stay in just because I had to, I always felt a twinge of jealousy and had a constant nagging feeling that she was two-timing me while I lay in bed. I never let on what I was thinking, but I am sure she gathered the way I felt by the different things I asked. That afternoon I asked if I could have a cigarette and Sister Shilton said that I could. It had been nearly eleven weeks since I'd had my last fag and after only having a couple of puffs my head was in a whirl. But I persevered and, after a little while, I began to get used to it again. Looking back now, oh, how I wish I had stopped then when fate had forced me to do so.

Jo and Tim returned with my footwear and stopped with me until late into the afternoon. Finally they said that they would have to be making a move for home, but would try and come up one day in the following week as they were on holiday. Then they were gone.

As usual Kate stopped over at her sister's relations', and

was back at the hospital first thing in the morning to visit me. She spent the whole day with me, just sitting beside my bed, chatting away about all kinds of things. She even sat there and watched me struggle to feed myself and the only time she left the ward was when she went down to the canteen for her lunch or up to the Jimmy Savile lounge for a cup of coffee. The Jimmy Savile lounge was a special room that he had had built, with comfortable chairs and a small kitchen where patients' families could go and make themselves a drink and relax for ten minutes. When she returned she told me who she had seen and talked to, as over the months she had got to know the families and friends of the other patients in the ward. She would always be sitting there, talking away, when her mum arrived to spend the afternoon with me before taking her back home. It was on this particular Sunday afternoon that she told me she would be on holiday the following week and her sister's in-laws had said that she would be welcome to stay there. 'I'll be able to come in and see you every day then, Andy, and you will be up in your wheelchair so I can push you round the hospital and that.'

It was really great news that I would have her near me all day and every day for a week. Kate and her mum spent the rest of the afternoon with me and then finally had to make a move. Saying goodbye wasn't as hard as usual as I knew that from next Sunday I was to have her with me every day for a week.

The following day as I lay on my side Lawrence came past my bed with a large box with 'Tricker' on it and took it into the small room that was attached to the ward. I had been pushed in there a couple of times when the cleaners wanted to polish the floor in the ward. It looked a bit like a junk room with old mattresses and empty boxes just thrown in.

'Hey, Lawrence! What's that you've got there, with my name on?' I asked.

'It's your wheelchair, Andy. I'm just going to put it together.'

67

Then I heard a voice from the other side of the ward: 'Your new model's arrived then, Andy? All right, lads, watch out, old Andy will soon be mobile!'

Guess who? Yer, you've got it. It was Frank warning the whole ward that I would soon be up and around.

That afternoon one of the occupational therapists arrived to see me. She was a short lady with white hair, the one who had come and bandaged my hands in the early days. She would put splints in my palms, then wrap two or three crepe bandages round them until I looked as if I was wearing boxing gloves. I kept them on in the early days, but as time went on I found that I couldn't do a thing with my hands bandaged up so, once she left, I would get at the bandages with my teeth until I finally had them unwrapped and my hands were free once again. But today it was not my hands she was interested in. She had come to measure me up for the collar I would need when I first got up to give my neck some extra support in the first couple of weeks. She took some measurements, then left to go back to her department. Half an hour later she returned with a foam collar in her hand.

'May I just try this on you, please?' She gently lifted my head and slipped the collar on.

'It's a good job I'm sitting up,' I said.

'Does it feel OK?' she asked.

'Well it feels a little tight. In fact, if you don't mind me saying, it feels as if it's cutting my chin.'

She removed it for a moment, took out a pair of scissors and trimmed a little piece off it, then put it back on. 'Oh that's much better, thanks,' I said.

Things were really starting to happen: my wheelchair had been delivered, I had been fitted out with my collar and was allowed to sit up for longer each day. That night on the telephone I brought everyone up to date on what had been happening.

The big day had now arrived. Sister Shilton told me in the

morning that that afternoon I would be getting up. I had no visitors coming in the afternoon and so had no worries about making a fool of myself. After lunch my bed was raised, a little at first, then a bit higher until I was sitting quite upright; then two of the orderlies, Lawrence and Barney, came over to my bed with Sister. 'There is no point in getting him dressed as he will only be up for a few minutes,' she said.

They pulled the curtains round my bed. Lawrence brought the wheelchair to the side of the bed and sister put on my collar. Then they pulled back the bedclothes.

'Are you OK, Andy? Lawrence, you take hold of the top half and Barney, you take the legs.'

I replied that I was OK, but inside my heart was beating ten to the dozen and I seemed to be breaking out in a cold sweat. The next thing I knew they were lifting me up, then lowering me into the wheelchair and that was the last thing I knew because I passed clean out. The next thing I knew I came to and I was back in bed.

'Are you all right, Andy?' I heard Sister Shilton saying to me.

'Hey, I'm sorry, Sister, I don't know what came over me,' I answered.

'Oh don't worry, you fainted, that's all. You're not the first and I don't suppose you will be the last. It was probably our fault: we didn't give you long enough sitting up in bed. Tomorrow we'll let you sit up longer before we try and get you in the wheelchair.'

They put my chair away again and left me lying there quietly. There was nothing I could do or say to stop myself from feeling such a fool. I kept telling myself I wasn't going to do tomorrow what I had done today.

The next day they raised my bed in the morning as well as the afternoon. It was well after lunch, I was still in bed and I knew I had Tim and Jo coming to see me. Then I saw Manuel and Barney coming over to my bed again. 'You be OK today, Andy,' Manuel said in his broken

English as he pulled the curtains round my bed.

Barney put my collar on for me and then the curtains flicked open and Sister came in. 'Do you feel better today, Andy?' she asked, and I said that I did.

'Try taking deep breaths as Manuel and Barney lift you.'

I did as she said while they lifted me off the bed and into the wheelchair. I was OK — I hadn't fainted. Barney lifted my feet onto the footplates of the chair and Manuel laid a sheet over me to cover my dignity.

'OK, Barney, open the curtain,' Sister said and she released the brakes on the chair and proceeded to push me down to the bottom of the ward, shouting as she went for someone to open the french doors at the bottom end. As she reached the doors I said, almost in a whisper, 'I think I'm going to faint again.'

'Oh no you don't,' Sister said and she tipped the wheelchair up onto its back wheels and told me to breathe in deeply. I did as I was told and the white, misty feeling in front of my eyes slowly faded away.

'Feel better?' she asked, and I acknowleged that I did so she gently lowered me again, telling me to take deep breaths all the time.

As she was telling me this I heard a familiar voice: 'Excuse me, Sister, could you tell me where my brother is?' It was Jo! She hadn't recognised me sitting there.

'He is here but he can't talk to you at the moment as he is finding it hard enough just to breathe,' she said. 'If you go for a coffee, by the time you get back he will be back into bed.' I, meanwhile, was trying to fill my lungs with oxygen that my brain was so desperately calling for. Sister Shilton tilted me back again until the dizzy feeling left me and then I was lowered again onto all four wheels. Those few agonising minutes felt like hours before she finally pushed me back up the ward and put me into bed.

'It won't always be like that, will it?' I asked.

'Oh no, with every day you will get better,' Sister Shilton said, smiling, as she walked away from my bed.

I should have realised that it wasn't going to be easy to get up after having spent nearly three months in bed. 'You must remember how weak you felt when you got up after being in bed for a week with the flu,' I told myself as I lay there.

I was still looking up at the ceiling and going over what had just taken place when Jo and Tim returned from the canteen. 'You're back in bed, then? I didn't even recognise you sitting there. Your hair, it's so long! It's half-way down your back,' Jo said. My hair had been fairly long before the accident and not being able to have it cut for so long it had grown very long. They were the first to see me in my wheelchair and I was to find out later what a shock it had been for Jo to see me sitting there. 'When I walked into the ward and he wasn't in his bed I thought he had been moved, but then when I went down to ask the Sister where he was and she said that it was him sitting there I couldn't believe it. He couldn't talk, he just sat there gasping for breath. He looked so pale and thin and his hair was right down his back. Oh he did look bad,' she told Mum.

For the next couple of days the pattern was the same as the last, only now I was given the button on my bed to operate, letting myself sit up more and more every few minutes. The dizziness would still occur even though I took every precaution to prevent it. I didn't get dressed, either, during those first couple of days. As soon as I was in the chair a sheet was laid over me and I was pushed down to the french windows at the bottom of the ward. There, as I continually fought to fill my lungs with that precious commodity, oxygen, I would sit looking out into the grounds of the hospital, trying to focus on one particular thing: a bench near one of the lawns or one of the trees that lined the drive or even one of the many cars in the car park on the opposite side of the drive. I would concentrate on one of these things for as long as I could until they would start to become a blur — almost as if a cloud of white mist had suddenly surrounded them — then I would have to quickly ask one of the orderlies to tip my chair back until the mist slowly disappeared and my brain had received the amount of oxygen that it needed.

By Saturday I had had several days in the wheelchair and I knew Mum, Dad and Lou were coming up to see me. Early in the morning Sister Shilton told me that I could get dressed that day. Later on two of the orderlies, Nicky and Lawrence, came over to dress me. 'What would you like to wear this morning? T-shirt and these jeans?' Lawrence asked as he held up a couple of things he had just taken out of my case.

'I don't mind,' I replied.

Then Lawrence produced a bag and strapped it to my leg. Something new that I had to contend with. I would have to wear a bag strapped to my leg to collect my urine. There are many words I can use, such as humiliating or degrading, but none can really express how I felt at having to wear this new piece of equipment. After putting the bag on they carried on with the job in hand, rolling me first to one side and then the other as they pulled on my pants and trousers. Then one sat me up while the other slipped my T-shirt on. They put my shoes and socks on and finally my collar. 'OK, Andy, you can start sitting yourself up whenever you're ready,' Lawrence said as he passed me the button control to my bed. Slowly, I let the bed rise up until I could see my legs and feet: there they were in an old pair of jeans that I remembered wearing, my feet in the new pair of training shoes that Tim had bought for me; I was wearing the T-shirt I had worn so many times before. I was completely dressed but I didn't feel dressed — why, I don't know, maybe because I hadn't dressed myself.

I sat there on the bed. It should have been a great day. I was dressed again, and with my parents due to see me for the first time in my wheelchair. But it was as if my insides had been put into a blender. I looked down at my motionless legs and at my toes and I said to myself, 'Please, toes, move for me again. Come on, you can do it. Only a little bit will do, just show me you can work again.'

I closed my eyes; the other lads were eating their lunch so no one was taking any notice. 'When I open my eyes, please, legs, be working again for me,' I kept saying to myself over and over again. But when I did look, they were still motionless. I gritted my teeth. Instead of letting my tears flow, I found I was becoming harder emotionally. 'Come on, Andy,' I told myself. 'One day they'll move again for you.' If I said if often enough I would convince myself, and my legs.

I was sitting down at the far end of the ward near the double doors continuing the battle to fill my lungs with oxygen when Mum, Dad and Lou arrived. They came and stood in front of me, said their hellos and then pulled chairs from the pile in the corner. They sat quietly beside me, not speaking either, because they had been warned that I would not be able to answer them, or because they could see the enormous effort it was costing me to breathe. They sat with me and watched as I called to be tipped back, then lowered again on to all four wheels. I had noticed over the last couple of days that I didn't need to be tipped back quite so often as on the first day that I had got out of bed. The family had been sitting with me for about a quarter of an hour when Lawrence came over and said that I would have to be put back to bed. Lawrence pushed me up the ward then he and Nicky lifted me back into bed. As they started to undress me I thought, 'Well, at this rate I won't get my clothes dirty,' as I had only had them on about half an hour. They pulled my sheets over me and then pulled the curtains back from around my bed.

Mum and Dad had been waiting just outside and when they saw the curtains go back they came straight over. 'Oh Andy, it was lovely to see you sitting up,' they said. To them it must have been, after only having seen me lying in bed for the last three months, but to me it was a bloody nightmare each time I left my bed and got into that wheelchair. They stayed with me, telling me all about what was going on back home and how they had celebrated the Queen's Silver Jubilee with the neighbours, having a drop of the old hard stuff and some eats on the large piece of grass outside our house. We carried on chatting until it was time for them to leave again. I was pleased they had seen me sitting up. I only hoped that by the time they came again, sometime during the coming week, I would have got over the dizziness and would be able to talk to them while I sat up. I think they left very happy after seeing me out of bed, but although I was pleased to be getting up, the dreams that I had had of being completely well by the time I had reached this point were quickly being broken. Perhaps when I start my therapy things will begin to happen, I told myself.

As I sat myself up each day I tried to do something to occupy my mind rather than dwell on the feeling of dizziness. I would listen to the radio and try to squeeze the rubber ball that Mum had given me so many weeks ago. Frank had also started to sit up a bit now and, as I sat there, he called over to me, 'Hey, Andy, how about throwing the ball over to me, then? I'll throw it back.'

I looked across and smiled, 'I'll have a go, mate, but I don't know where it will end up.' I still could not grip with my hands and could only hold something by extending my wrist upwards: this would make my fingers curl under and enable me to hold something gently. I moved my arm to the side and tried to throw the ball to Frank but instead of going to him it ended up half-way down the ward. This was greeted with laughter from both patients and staff who were watching. Marcia retrieved it and then suggested I should have another go.

'Here goes then!' I said as I tried to throw it one more time. It was a bit better and it landed beside Frank's locker. I had several attempts before the ball finally reached its correct destination which was greeted with a big cheer. Over the coming days I eventually got quite accurate. I would throw the ball and then he would return it in the same way. Mind you, we still needed to call upon the assistance of one of the nurses from time to time when for some reason my accuracy failed me.

Chapter 10
First Physio

I was out of bed and sitting in my chair when Jane came to see me one day.

'Oh, there you are,' she said as she walked down the ward towards me. 'How would you like a trip round the hospital?'

I did not really jump with joy at the prospect, but before I could say yes or no she had removed the brakes and begun to push me through the ward.

'Where are you off to?' Frank called as we passed his bed.

'For the grand tour,' I replied.

Before we reached the door of the ward I noticed a kitchen and a large bathroom with three or four sinks on the right and the Sister's office on the left. I had not seen these before as on previous times when I had been pushed to and fro to the different departments of the hospital I had been in my bed, so all that I had been able to see was the ceiling. It was odd to think that even places like these, so much a part of the ward, were new to me. We turned right outside the ward and as Jane pushed me up the long corridor I noticed that Wards Two and Two X were not the only wards in this hospital and that it wasn't only men who broke their necks. The wards started from One X and went right up to Four and Four X, the last two being ladies' wards. Opposite

Ward Four X was one of the physio departments and as Jane pushed me through the doors I saw men and women doing various things. There were some lying on large mats rolling from side to side; others, who looked as if they were trying to walk with stiff legs, were in parallel bars. I thought, 'Why the hell don't they bend their legs,' because at this point in time I did not realise they were wearing callipers under their trousers. These enabled them to lock their knees and without them even standing up would have been impossible. There were others pulling weights in an effort to build muscles in their arms.

Jane bopped down beside me. 'You'll be coming up here in a couple of days, and we'll get you out onto a mat and put you through your paces.' As I looked around I realised I wasn't looking at anybody in particular but at a reflection of myself in weeks to come.

Jane turned my chair around and proceeded back down the corridor towards the ward. 'That was a pretty short tour,' I said as we came level with the door of the ward, but instead of going in we went straight past, then past One X and then turned right.

'Where are we off to now?' I asked.

'Just up here and through these doors is the hydro pool.' She pushed me through two sets of double doors and as we entered the room the warm dense heat hit us.

'Crumbs, it's hot in here, isn't it?' I gasped and Jane explained that being in a hydro pool was like being in a warm bath. I suddenly remembered that it was through here that I had come when I first arrived at this hospital all those weeks ago.

Jane turned my chair around again and pushed me back down the corridor along which we had come; then we turned right and as we passed along a new corridor I noticed the theatre and X-Ray departments that I had frequently visited over the last three months; then it was down another long corridor, passing through the main foyer, past the canteen where my visitors went for a cup of tea and then, at the bottom, came to another physio department.

'Eventually you will come here to use this one rather than the one near the ward,' Jane informed me.

'Why's that, Jane?' I asked.

'Well, the one near the ward is mainly used when you first get out of bed, but once you are stronger then we make you come all the way down here as getting here and back is therapy in itself.'

'You're not kidding!' I thought to myself as this main corridor was about three or four hundred yards long.

She pushed me back the same way we had come, but as we neared Ward One X we turned right and down into a huge hall. At the far end I could see four large targets and at the near end were a couple of lads with bows and arrows.

'This is where the old archery takes place then, is it?' I thought. I watched as one of them strung his bow with one of the arrows that lay across his lap, then fired at the target. 'I think I'll enjoy doing that,' I said to myself as Jane pushed me back to the ward. She parked me beside my bed and then said she had got to go and see to one of her other patients. I had seen most of the hospital but there were still some places I hadn't seen; there was the Occupational Therapy department, the Jimmy Savile lounge and the Sports Centre to name a few. Nevertheless, I was quite pleased with my grand tour.

As I sat beside my bed I tried to take in all that I had seen. Then I heard Frank call over to me. 'How was the tour? What do the different places look like?' he asked and I tried to explain all that I had seen. It was at times like this, when I started to talk too much, that the dizziness would come over me again. I suppose I was not filling my lungs up enough, so I had to call Lawrence over to tip me back before I blacked out. Once I had been tipped back for a few moments I would be OK again. While this was going on Frank and I had broken off our conversation, so I was sitting there quietly when suddenly I thought to myself, 'Why not have a go at moving my chair a little way on my own?' I laid my hands on the wheels and tried to push it. It took all my effort to move only about six inches and with the effort that I had used I quickly had to breathe in deeply to stop myself from feeling faint again. I had been sitting there, imagining myself up on those parallel bars next week, when in reality it took all my effort to move my wheelchair only a matter of inches. I decided to sit still again until Lawrence and Nicky came over to put me back into bed.

Once I was back in bed and they had left me I went over what had happened during the last couple of days. Although I was pleased to be getting up, I realised what an uphill struggle I had got before me when I considered that I could hardly even move my chair. Should I lie back and give up right here and now or should I fight to improve? There I was, rationally confronting myself with all my opportunities and deciding to choose the latter and give it all I'd got. There was never really another choice: if I had given up and remained in bed I would have slowly faded away and probably died of pressure sores or some other complaint.

On Monday Kate came to Aylesbury for her week's holiday. She arrived after lunch when I was dressed and sitting in my chair. 'Hi, babe,' she said as she bent down and kissed me, 'it's nice to see you with some clothes on.' It had been a long time since she had seen me in my old jeans and T-shirt. We sat near my bed and she told me that her sister's in-laws, Mr and Mrs Causbrook, would be coming to pick her up later that evening. We were still talking when I noticed Jane coming towards us.

'How are you feeling? Ready to come down to the physio department?' she said.

'Well, I've got Kate here. She's come to spend the week with me,' I answered.

'Well, that's OK. Kate can come with you if she wants.' So off we went — Jane pushing me and Kate walking along beside me.

Jane manouvered my chair up alongside a bench which

had a soft seating on it, then she called one of the other physiotherapists over. 'OK, Andy, we are going to lift you onto this bench.' Jane took the top half and Penny took hold of me at the back. She asked Kate if she would position the large mirror that she had previously pulled near to where I was sitting in front of me. As I looked into the mirror I could see Jane standing behind me but, more to the point, who was this other person that I saw in this mirror? For the first time I was able to see for myself how much I had changed: my face was very pale and drawn, my once wavy hair was long and straight, my arms and chest that had once been full of muscle were now just a matter of skin and bone — was it really me sitting here with this collar round my neck?

Then I heard Jane say, 'OK, Andy. Now, I've got hold of you, but I want you to look at yourself in that mirror and when I let go of you, see if you can sit there without me holding you.' Jane let go, and as she did I immediately fell back into her again as there was nothing for me to lean against.

'OK, let's try again.' This time I fell to my right.

'Now look at your chest and stomach muscles, use your shoulders and arms to balance, now hold your arms out to the side like you would if you were going to balance along a beam.'

We tried again and by really concentrating on myself I managed to sit there for a matter of seconds before I fell back into Jane once again.

'All right, Andy, that will do for today,' Jane said and she asked Penny again if she would mind giving her a hand to lift me back into my chair. Then Jane pushed me back to the ward.

After Jane had gone, Kate spoke. 'Hey, babe, you done well.'

'Don't lie, Katie. Why don't you tell the truth? I'm bloody useless.' As I said the words it was as if all my insides were screwing up.

'Don't say that, Andy, you can't expect to be brilliant at

your first effort but it will come, you'll see,' she said. As I sat there I just wanted to bury my head in my hands and cry my eyes out, but after what I had been through in the previous three months there did not seem to be any tears left. Although I was allowed out of bed after lunch I was having to be put back in bed again before tea and I would always have to have my backside checked to make sure there were no pressure sores. Kate sat chatting with me till late into the evening when Mr and Mrs Causbrook came to pick her up. It is only now, as I think back, that I realised what Kate had to put up with; not only a change in my looks but also coping with my many disappointments. Time and again she picked up the pieces and rebuilt my dreams.

As the next couple of days passed they took on the same pattern as the previous one: Kate would arrive early in the morning and sit with me as I increased the sitting up movement on my bed; then, after lunch, I would be lifted off my bed and into my chair where I would be allowed to sit quietly and get used to the adjustment from bed to chair; then Jane would arrive and wheel me up to the physio department where I would practise sitting unaided. I know it must seem a simple thing, a matter of just sitting there. It would have seemed simple to me until I had this accident, but now I had to look at myself and concentrate very hard on what I was doing. It became easier, though, as each day passed.

Slowly, I graduated to the point where I had to learn to lift my hands above my head and then hold them out so that they were pointing in front of me. The only trouble with this was that I had to learn my limitations. If I moved them up or out too far or too fast I would tip forward and end up in a heap on the floor — if no one was close enough to catch me. After my trials and tribulations in the physio department Kate would either push me back to the ward or we would take a quick tour round the hospital, always ending up at the canteen to buy something to eat or a packet of fags. Then we would return to the ward and I would have to be put back to bed. Kate would spend the rest of the day and evening sitting beside my bed, either talking or reading. I realised that it couldn't be much of a holiday for her (the same as it couldn't have been much for my parents a week or so earlier) but for me, I couldn't have asked for anything more. That week seemed to pass so much quicker than all the others that I had spent since I had been at Stoke Mandeville — perhaps because I was now getting out of bed, but somehow I think it had something to do with Kate being there with me every day. Mum and Dad had been up already during the week, but inevitably the weekend came and it was time for Kate to leave. It had been great having her with me but I knew that she had to leave to return to work the following day. We said our goodbyes and she said that she would phone during the week and would be up to see me next weekend.

At the weekends the hospital seemed almost to come to a stop. There was no therapy as most of the physiotherapists were off duty, except the ones who were on duty to give therapy to those who were in bed. On the Sunday after Kate's holiday I sat in my chair waiting for my visitors to arrive and thinking of what I would have been doing if I was back home. I had always enjoyed my weekends. It was very rare for me to be out of bed before twelve on Saturday, then I would have a quick wash, get dressed and have breakfast all in a matter of minutes. Then I would slip off out to The Grange to have a few games of pool, and probably buy myself a pie or something for my lunch. When closing time arrived I would jump on my moped and make my way to the local park. There I would meet a couple of the local girls who I knew would be down there. If Kate hadn't been working at her Saturday job this wouldn't have been possible. Besides, I am sure she chatted up blokes on Monday nights when she went into town to the Corn Exchange disco so really I was only getting my own back! Anyway, enough of this tit-for-tat stuff! I would spend most of the afternoon with these two girls and, as I've told you before, I enjoyed the company of the opposite sex — not that I was funny in any way — I suppose I was keeping my eye out just in case Kate and I finished (which we frequently did). After I left the girls I would return home for my tea, then get changed and go off up to Kate's for the evening. At the time I was remembering, we were going through a bit of a sticky patch. I think we both wanted to finish it but didn't quite know how to do it. When it got around ten o'clock I would make my excuses and leave, knowing full well that I was going to join another girlfriend who was baby sitting. Although I knew I was two-timing Kate, I couldn't help myself, as the girl I was going to see was probably the only other one I would have liked to have gone out with if I had not been going out with Kate. And then, if I really faced the truth, I was sure Kate was two-timing me on Monday nights, so knowing this helped ease my conscience. After spending an enjoyable couple of hours with my babysitter friend, I would finally arrive home after midnight. So now you know why I never got out of bed before twelve on Sunday either.

I was still reminiscing about Saturdays when I saw my visitors arriving. Mum wasn't coming today, instead Dad, Terry and the two girls (my younger sister, Lou, and Terry's daughter, Jackie) came. I sat there, dressed and with my collar on, as they walked towards me.

'Hello, Andy. How are you?' Dad and Terry said as they reached my chair.

'Oh I'm not too bad, thanks,' I replied, and tried to smile at the same time. Both Jackie and Lou smiled back.

'It's good to be out of that bed, isn't it?' Terry asked.

'Yer, it is really, I suppose,' I replied, 'but I feel dizzy from time to time and I really hate wearing this collar — it makes me feel claustrophobic.'

Dad spoke then. 'How about going up to the Jimmy Savile lounge? We have bought all the things we need to make a cup of tea instead of having to go down to the canteen.'

I must admit I wasn't thrilled at the idea, but Dad had turned and walked over to one of the nurses and I could hear him asking if it would be all right for them to take me out of the ward. I saw the nurse nodding, and off we went: Dad pushing with Terry and the two girls walking beside me. Instead of going through the hospital to get to the lounge Dad pushed me out through the French doors at the bottom of the ward. It was a very hot August day and as I went down the little slope just outside the doors I felt the rays from the sun on my face. As I looked across the grounds, I remembered seeing the same sights a week or so earlier, when I had had to concentrate on them to stop myself from fainting. Now I was being pushed along a narrow path past the front of the other wards that were on the same side as mine. As I looked at the outsides of the wards, I realised that they had once been old army huts put up during the Second World War. Suddenly we came to a new brick building with a large piece of concrete in front of it dotted with large flower pots. Dad pushed me over the concrete and into the lounge. It looked very smart, with carpet on the floor and modern chairs with coffee tables in front of them. Dad parked me near one of the tables and then went off to the kitchen to make the tea. I sat chatting to Jackie and Lou while Dad and Terry made the tea, but as I sat there I started to feel really warm and the collar round my neck made things even worse as I imagined it was stopping me from breathing properly. Dad and Terry returned with the tray of tea.

'Dad, you couldn't loosen this collar for me, could you, please? I can't seem to breathe properly,' I asked as Dad approached my chair.

'I don't know if I should, Andy.'

'Oh come on, Dad, it won't hurt. It's been nearly two weeks since I got up.'

With that Dad did as I asked and loosened the fasteners at the back of the collar. I can't begin to explain what a relief it was to be able to move my Adam's apple freely again.

As Terry began to pour the tea, I realised I had something

new to contend with. Although I had sat in the ward and let someone stand beside me holding a cup of tea with a straw in it so that I could drink, I was now to perform in front of people whom I did not know and who did not know me. Mind you, as they were probably visiting relations in the hospital, they, no doubt, must have had to do the same for them, but it did not stop me feeling that all their eyes were on me as I drank my tea through the straw. We finished our tea and then returned to the ward where we sat near my bed and chatted until it was time for me to get back into bed. I was gradually being allowed to stay in my chair for longer periods each day. It was nearly tea time by the time I was undressed and put back into the safety and comfort of my bed. Dad, Terry and the girls stayed with me until after tea, then finally made their way back home.

Although it had turned seven o'clock, it had been a very warm and humid day, and I lay there with the large window behind my bed flung wide open and only a cotton sheet covering me. The telly was on and some of the other lads still had their visitors with them. Although the sounds of their voices drifted over to where I lay, it seemed to be in the background of my mind as I was consciously thinking of other things: what tomorrow and beyond had in store for me.

Chapter 11
Looking After Myself Again

Monday and the start of a new week. My visitors were still coming to see me during the week, but now they would often have to wait while I finished my therapy. Mum and Dad often arrived to find me not in the ward but down in the physio department. Mum very rarely went there as she couldn't bear to see me struggle to do the simplest of things. I had progressed from sitting in front of the mirror to being lifted out of my chair onto one of the large mats that lay along the left hand side of the room; there I would start off lying on my back, then Jane would bend my legs up until my knees touched my chest and then lower them down again; then I was rolled over onto my stomach, and she bent my legs up until the heels of my feet touched my buttocks. There would be the usual creaks from my limbs and joints as they were being positioned in the various places. After this, Jane would sit me up then, by kneeling behind me, she would gently push me forward, at the same time asking me to try and reach out and touch my toes. As she leant on me to get me to lean that bit further forward, again I would hear the familiar creaks from the vertebrae in my spine as they, too, were being asked to stretch to their limits. Then I was allowed to lie back for a few minutes to rest before trying to roll myself over onto my side, and from there onto my elbow and finally to a sitting position. It was impossible for me to simply sit up from the lying position. I would spend an hour or more on the mat before I was finally lifted back into my chair. The only trouble was that after lying down I would feel quite giddy until I got used to being back in the sitting position once again. That was all the therapy I had to start with, but I can tell you it really took all the energy that I could muster just to do those few exercises on that mat.

As the days passed I seemed to improve at the different exercises that were asked of me and so, after finishing on the mat, I would move over to a new piece of equipment. My chair was positioned between two cords that came down from the ceiling and which had things on the end for me to put my hands in; on the other end of the cords were two bags with weights in. When I pulled downwards, the bags of weights would rise. When I raised my arms the bags would come down again. I pulled on those cords as many times as I could and, as each day passed, I tried to improve on what I had done the previous day. Those pulleys, as they were called, improved the strength in my arms no end.

One day, after I had been doing really well at the pulleys and Jane was pushing me to the ward, she suddenly said, 'Well I think you can make it back by yourself from here.' We were only about half-way back and I was already shattered by what I'd done in the physio department, without having to shove myself the rest of the way along the corridor to the ward.

'Sure you wouldn't like to push me back?'

'Go on,' she said encouragingly, 'you can make it.'

I started pushing. Although it wasn't very quick, at least I was making progress. Slowly but surely I made my way along the corridor, moving a little way then stopping as my arms felt like lead weights and almost ready to drop off. I reached One X and only had about ten yards to go before I finally got to my ward, but those ten yards seemed more like fifty. As I turned into the ward, Nicky must have seen how tired I looked as he quickly came over and pushed me down to the far end where he parked me at one of the large tables. I was just in time for afternoon tea and I can tell you I wasn't half ready for a cup!

I was sitting at the table, just finishing my tea, when one of the occupational therapists came up to me.

'Hello, Andy,' she said. 'Are you doing anything at the moment because I just thought you might like to come and have a look at the Occupational Therapy department with me?'

She was a young girl (about twenty, I would have said) and as I was never a one for passing up an opportunity to go somewhere with a young lady I said, 'Yer, why not? As long as I don't have to do anything as I've only just got back from physio and I'm pretty tired out.'

She released the brakes on my chair and pushed me up and out of the ward. We turned right along the same corridor as if I was going to therapy, but turned left before we reached it, then went along another corridor and I noticed that it had got quite an incline to it as we reached the end and went into the department. Sue (I found out her name) pushed me into a large room where there were several tables dotted around. Several people in wheel-chairs were sitting round them doing different things. There were two or three doing basket work, a couple of women knitting, a young lad trying to hold a pen and write with it and another learning to hold a knife and fork again with what little use he had got left in his once perfect hands.

'Most people who need to come up here usually come in the mornings and leave the afternoons for their physio-therapy,' Sue said. She turned my chair round and pushed me along a small corridor. As we passed different doors she showed me a bathroom where I could learn to brush my hair and teeth again, and wash my own face and hands and hair — something I was longing to do; a place where I could learn to lift myself in and out of a bath if I got enough strength back into my arms. We moved on past the toilets to a room with several typewriters.

'You can learn how to type if you want,' Sue said.

Then we moved along a bit further, through what I gathered was a woodwork department from the lathes and piles of sawdust on the floor; finally we came to a room with several screens. Sue pushed past them and I saw four beds.

'This is where you will come to learn how to dress yourself again.'

So there it was, my grand tour of the occupational therapy department. There wasn't that much to see but I knew that in the coming weeks I would be spending quite a lot of time here. Sue turned and pushed me back to the ward, then left me sitting near my bed to contemplate what I had seen before the orderlies came to put me back to bed.

Although the ward came alive very early in the mornings, by the time I had been washed and dressed and got used to sitting up in bed, a good part of the morning had gone before I was finally put into my chair. I began to realise that this was not the nurses' fault but mine, so I started to cut down the time it took to get used to sitting up from lying down. On the following couple of mornings, I forced myself to ignore the feeling of faintness that I had felt as I tried to get up, and by doing so managed to be up well before ten o'clock, which was good compared to the time I had been taking.

Now that I was able to get up earlier my therapy started in earnest. I had been put down to go to the hydro pool twice a week and the morning came for my first time. The other lads had dispersed to their different therapies by the time I emerged from the curtains that had been pulled round my bed whilst I had my trunks pulled on. Lawrence wrapped a large sheet round me to hide my blushes as well as to keep me warm, then pushed me out of the ward and down to the pool. We went through the two sets of double doors and again the warm, dense heat hit me.

Lawrence pushed me to the side of the pool and then

called to an oldish lady on the other side: 'I've brought Andy Tricker — it's his first time!'

'OK, Lawrence,' the lady replied and with that he turned and walked away.

As I sat there I watched as the older lady and her helper positioned another fella's chair beside a strange piece of equipment. Together they lifted him out of his chair and placed him on it. Then, with a turn of a handle, he slowly rose above the edge of the pool. He was swung out and over the water and lowered into the arms of the physiotherapist who had been standing in the pool waiting for him. Now it was my turn and I went through exactly the same procedure as the one I had just watched. The winch mechanism lowered me down into the pool, but it was not until it reached my chest that I found out how warm the water really was. I was also extremely lucky to find my own physiotherapist, Jane, waiting to take hold of me (the therapists in the pool worked on a rotary basis, all taking a turn in the pool every month). Jane told me to put my arms round her neck, then she slipped both arms underneath me, carried me across the pool and sat me on a ledge that was well below the water level. She stood between my legs.

'Well, what do you think of it, then?' she asked.

'Yer, it's OK. It's really nice to be submerged in water again,' I replied. Then she began to manipulate my limbs — first bending and straightening my legs, then moving onto my arms, hands and fingers. Jane then let me sit there for a few minutes before taking me back to the chairlift. Although I had only been in the bath for about a quarter of an hour, the warmth of the water and the exercises that she had put me through had left me with very little strength. The two ladies lifted me back into my chair, then dried me before wrapping the large sheet around me again to keep me warm while I was pushed back to the ward. As soon as I got back, Lawrence and Nicky lifted me onto my bed and dressed me. After being dressed I did not get straight back into my chair, but instead sat on my bed as it truly had taken an awful lot out of me. However, I was glad that I had been to the baths and was already looking forward to the next time that I was due to go.

Not only was I swimming two mornings a week now, I was also attending occupational therapy on the other three mornings. Someone would come and fetch me and push me to the department. I started off trying to do a few simple things such as holding a pen or knife and fork. It may sound easy but having lost the ability to grip anything with any great force, it was much harder than it sounds. When holding the pen I found I could not apply enough pressure to write anything clearly, so Sue advised me to try a felt-tip pen. This I did and found that I could write quite clearly with it. Mind you, my hand was a bit shaky to start with and I found that although I started with straight lines, towards the end of the page they would go up hill. As I practised it seemed to improve greatly. While I was practising my writing I remembered what my old English teacher used to say: 'Andrew, it looks just as if a spider has crawled across your page. It's a job just to try and make head or tail of what you have written!' I thought, 'I wonder what she would say if she could see this.'

Then came the next task: to hold my knife and fork. I did not want to rely on straps to hold them for me and so worked out a technique of threading the handle of the fork through my fingers, giving me enough control to spear different pieces of food. I practised on pieces of banana or apple so as not to spoil my lunch. Then came the knife! That was a bit more difficult, but I found the easiest way round was to clasp it between both hands and then cut up all my food before actually starting to eat it. I hope I am explaining this clearly. Anyway, after much practice I no longer pushed my food off the edge of the plate but was able to spear different pieces of food quite effectively. This took time, of course, and there were many times when I became very frustrated and felt like throwing the plate of chopped banana all over the floor, but I'm proud to say that I never quite reached that point.

After overcoming those two difficulties I moved onto the bathroom. The sink was designed so I could wheel myself right up close to it. Now came the task of washing and doing all the other things that we all do each and every morning. The first job was to fill the basin with water which I accomplished quite well. Then came the job of wetting and soaping the flannel. Once again, not having sufficient grip made things that much more difficult. I learnt not to get the soap too wet or to drop it into the sink full of water. If I did I would have to spend five minutes trying to retrieve it. To wring out the flannel, I had to squeeze it between the palms of both hands in the same way as I held my knife. I also used this technique to hold my toothbrush, but before I could brush my teeth I had to take the top off the paste (this is when the things I was about to brush came in handy — to take the top off and also to replace it!). I used my teeth in similar ways to do things like taking the top off a pen. I then moved on to brushing my hair. I had to use a brush rather than a comb as it was easier to hold the handle of a brush. After a while I became quite good at making myself look respectable again. As my mum always said, 'Where there's a will there is always a way.'

After occupational therapy or swimming, whichever of the two I was doing that morning, I would return to the ward for lunch — always on the agenda between the hours of twelve and one. After this it was off to physiotherapy and time to be put through my paces physically. I enjoyed the physiotherapy more than the occupational as in my mind I believed that the more work I did and the harder I worked at my exercises the more likely I would be to get back the use of my muscles and my limbs. I would be put through my paces first on the mat and then finish off by doing as many pulleys as I could. Jane would push me half-way back to the ward, leaving me to push myself the remaining three hundred yards. It would be around three in the afternoon and time for tea when I reached the tables at the far end of the ward. We always had tea and bread and jam or marmite

91

or sandwich spread even though we had a hot evening meal at six every evening. There was no more therapy after tea and I would stay in the ward with the other lads. More often than not I had visitors who would either wait in the ward for me or come to look for me and wait until I finished therapy, then give me a push back to the ward. I would spend the rest of the afternoon chatting with them until it was time for them to leave. I still had many visitors during the week, like my friends, Dot and George, or my foreman from work, Ken Collinson, and, of course, Mum, Dad, Kate, my sisters and their husbands, my brother and his wife (who still came every Wednesday) and my dear friends, Chris and Terry, and their kids, Jackie and Darren, who were regular visitors. After whoever had been to see me had gone (usually around six to seven in the evening) I took the chance to return to bed, as by that time I was very tired from all the therapy I had done during the day. I can tell you, I never needed much rocking before I was well away in The Land of Nod.

Not only had I improved physically over the last few weeks but so had all the other lads who had come into the ward at roughly the same time as me. Frank, Keith, the two Peters and even the old boy, Les were now all up in their wheelchairs. Although we were all improving physically, we were all suffering some kind of emotional problem, either with girlfriends or wives and families. It was when your girlfriend rang up to say she was off out that night to a disco — that's when that dreaded emotion, jealousy, raised its evil head and screwed all your insides up and sent your mind imagining all kinds of things: like, what if she meets some bloke and starts going out with him or what if she goes back to his place and so on. Or it might have been something like the wife and kids hadn't turned up and the different fellas were wondering where they had got to; was his best mate being a bit more than just helpful? Or something completely different would get you down, brought on by the fact that when you're in hospital you are completely without any privacy whatsoever, and there is nowhere you can get away to be on your own. It might be that you have been confronted with a problem in physio and you hadn't been able to achieve whatever it was you wanted to do and inside you felt really useless. You would try to tell your visitor, perhaps the person who was really closest to you what had happened, and they would turn round and say, 'Well dear, it doesn't matter, does it?' or 'Never mind, you'll do it soon.' I know words like that were meant to comfort but you could see your friends almost ready to explode as they had come to the end of their tether and no one seemed to understand. That's when the voices would start to rise and tears begin to flow — either from one of the lads or from the ones they loved. And sometimes it would be like that for me, too.

Chapter 12
Up on my feet
after five months

August had come to an end and I was about to embark on my fourth month in hospital. Although it had been three months, the week days no longer dragged on like they had done in the beginning, but unfortunately I could not say the same for the week-ends. I know this was the time when I had the majority of my visitors but, oddly enough, they did not compensate for not being able to do something constructive during the day. I thought what a waste the weekends were, when I could have been doing more therapy and so improving myself physically that much quicker. But thinking on it more deeply now, I realise how essential it must have been for the physiotherapists to have a break from us patients. Undoubtedly we must have got them down — not only with our physical difficulties but with our emotional problems. We all spent the majority of the day with our personal therapists and I believe we all confided in them, not only about our fears and anxieties but with the inner feelings or doubts that came to us over and over again.

Like I said, my visitors were still coming to see me very

regularly and I do not think there is anything that can take the place of actually seeing someone you love or like to call a friend. The only trouble with having them there with you for most of the day was the time after they left. I was now able to wheel myself down to the French doors at the bottom of the ward, and I could sit there and watch them walk across the car park and jump into their cars. As they drove up the long drive they would wave continually until they were finally out of sight. I was seventeen now, but it took all my inner strength to hold back the tears that I so desperately wanted to shed. I knew I could not let myself cry, because I had to turn my chair round to face all the lads in the ward and I could not let them see how emotional I really felt. So, I would bite my tongue, then turn and push myself past the two tables where they were sitting and then up and out of the ward and into the main corridor just outside the ward. There I would park my chair with the back against the wall. By now most of the lights had been turned off, there was only the occasional one throwing out a very dim light. There I would sit, wallowing in my own self pity. Then, like changing a record, I would change my thoughts and let them bully me. 'Don't be so pathetic,' I would say. 'Keep on believing you are going to improve and that one of these days you will be walking across the car park and getting into a car and going home.' After putting myself through a confrontation like this, which I did at very regular intervals, I would return to the ward, able to face the other lads and join in their conversation or even play a game of cards which, I might add, I frequently lost.

By the middle of August I was becoming much stronger as each day and week passed and was able to push myself all the way from the physio department back to the ward. The corridors were always full of wheelchairs going in each direction: some moving very slowly like mine, others would shoot past me at an incredible speed, and it was funny to watch people who were visiting or even staff jump out of the way of a wheelchair going at top speed. I usually finished my therapy by two o'clock and would make my way back to the ward. I pushed myself several yards, then stopped for a breather. The first corridor that I had to go up was about four hundred yards long and rose every hundred yards or so. This made it fine when going down, but on the return journey — well that's why I had to stop for several breathers. One particular day I noticed another of Jane's patients a little way ahead of me and decided that I was going to beat him back to the wards if it killed me. As I reached the foyer he was only about twenty yards in front of me, but at this point I had to push myself over the edge of a large piece of carpet and this made the job of pushing my chair twice as hard until I reached the other side of the carpet and was on tiled floor covering again. I began to cut back the distance that he had gained upon me, and as we reached the end of the main corridor I was only a matter of feet behind him. We had both continually stopped for breathers and, although I could not say for certain, I am sure he knew what I was trying to do. My arms were aching all the way from my wrists to my shoulders but I refused to give into the pain and tiredness that I felt. I knew that if I was to beat him I would have to carry on pushing when he stopped for his next breather and this is what I did. As I passed him I said, 'Hello' as if there had not been anything going on between us. I kept on pushing until I was several feet ahead of him and then stopped for a well-earned breather. I sat there and thought, 'Well, if he goes and overtakes me there is no way that I will have the strength to overtake him again.' But to my joy there was no challenge from him. It was as if he had surrendered — if that's the right word. I pushed myself along the corridor and then turned into the ward. I was so pleased inside at the challenge I had set myself and at having achieved what I had set out to do that it was not until later that I realised what had been a great boost to my morale must have been a great blow to his.

One day, when I had just finished another exhausting hour or so in the physio department and was about to push myself back to the ward I felt someone take hold of the back of my chair and begin to push me. I turned and saw Jane.

'What do I owe this unexpected pleasure to, then?' I asked.

'Oh, you'll see,' she said as she pushed me along the corridor. We turned and carried on along the next corridor, but instead of turning into the ward, Jane pushed me into the hall where the archery took place.

'Hello, Peter. This is Andy — it's his first time,' Jane said as she wheeled me into the hall.

'Hello, Andy.' He was an oldish man with white hair and he was dressed in white flannels and shirt as if he had been playing cricket or something.

'Hello,' I replied.

He then tested my arms to see how much strength I had. 'OK. We will try you with this bow to start with,' he said, 'but first I will have to bandage you up.' He began by bandaging a splint round my left arm at the elbow so it was locked out straight, then he buckled a device onto my right hand which had a hook that came up in front of my index finger. This was hooked onto the string of the bow, so that I could pull the string back. He then proceeded to bandage my hand, tucking the rest of my fingers out of the way. Then he bandaged the bow to my left hand and with a final bandage he strapped me into my chair to prevent me from falling out. He pushed me over to the line where the others were, so that I was sideways on to the target at the far end of the ward.

'OK, then, you hook the arrow on like so, then you straighten your left arm so the bow is in line with the target. That's right. Now hook that little hook on your right hand onto the string and pull it back. That's it. Now, just turn your wrist outwards and bingo!' The arrow shot off the bow and hit the curtains at the far end of the hall.

'Well you didn't hit the target,' said Peter, 'but not many people do straight away. Right, let's have another go.' He strung my bow for me again and pointed out what I had done wrong first time. This time I hit the target, but only on the outer rim.

'Well done,' he said. Then he placed another arrow on my bow. After I had fired all six arrows Peter and his helper retrieved the arrows, calling out where I had hit the target — either in the blue, red or yellow (or as they like to call it, gold) which I hasten to add I did not hit. Peter returned with all the arrows for myself and for all the others who were doing archery at that time, then we were away again. First he would place an arrow on my bow and then one on the person next to me.

I spent a good three quarters of an hour firing arrows down at the target and as time went on became better and better and even managed to get a couple of golds. When it was time to finish Peter removed all the bandages and checked to see that the circulation in my hands was all right after having had them strapped up for that length of time.

'You've done very well for your first time,' he said, 'are you coming again tomorrow?'

'Yes, I would like to,' I replied, and he nodded as if to say 'see you tomorrow' and with that I pushed myself back to the ward. As I trundled along I felt my arms aching again. I had not realised how much of my strength pulling the bow back had taken out of me. I realised that not only had archery been something I could enjoy, but it was also another way of building my muscles up. I returned to the ward just in time for afternoon tea, and feeling very hungry and thirsty after all my efforts in the physio department and then in the archery class.

Kenny (the lad who had been injured in the army truck) had left Stoke Mandeville and gone to a hospital much closer to his home town of Newcastle. Also, others had left, mainly the ones that were up in their wheelchairs at the same time when I was still in bed. You knew they were getting close to leaving when they began to go home for weekends. This was to get them used to coping on their own, and also to help their families overcome the difficulties that they would undoubtedly face.

As each patient left there was always a new arrival to take his place and who would be put at the beginning of the ward, where I had first been. It might be a young man or an old man, every patient came from a different walk of life, but every one of them had had an accident which had brought them to Stoke Mandeville. There was Mac, who I could only describe as a devout Christian; Tommy, who had been serving on the Ark Royal in the Navy, and Dave, who was a motor mechanic. Then there was Ernie, an old boy, who invariably called out during the day and night. He had been a builder and had fallen from his ladder. In doing so he had not only broken his neck but had also got severe concussion. There were times when he swore there was someone trying to push him out of his bed. This was not true of course, but all the reasoning in the world could not stop him from believing what he truly thought was happening. This kind of accident is hard on anyone, but it seemed to me that it was hardest on the young such as myself or the very old like Ernie and another old boy, Les. Les had been in the ward as long as I had and was more unfortunate than most. He had been out playing bowls then, as he was walking across a zebra crossing, he was knocked down by a motor cyclist and broke his neck. But instead of losing the use of his legs and keeping some movement in his arms, in his case it was the other way round. He was up in a wheelchair, but although he could manoeuvre his chair around by using his feet he had to have all the other tasks, such as feeding, done for him. I don't know which I would have preferred — to have movement in my legs with the prospect of maybe walking again, but having to rely on someone to dress me and so on, or be the way I was, able to hope that one day I would be able to do everything for myself except the one thing I wanted to do most — walk. It was really a 'catch twenty-two' situation, where the best solution would have been to be able to do everything again for myself and that was only

99

going to happen if I made a complete recovery.

Although there were all these lads in the ward, over the months I had become closest to Frank and Keith. Now that they too had got out of bed and were in wheelchairs they had somehow regained their will and enthusiasm for life as their strength returned with all the therapy they did. They somehow took over the ward, charging to and fro and always doing something or other to relieve the boredom during the day and evenings. It was about this time that I told Mum and Dad I thought I could manage without visitors during the week. This would help me to get on with my therapy during the day without any interruptions and in the evenings as well. Even if they did come they would have to leave by seven o'clock so I would have been on my own in the evening anyway. At first it was hard not seeing a familiar face from back home and by the time the weekend arrived I could not wait to see my family and friends. I think I appreciated them more having not seen them for a week; but although I thought no one would be coming during the week, not many weeks went by without my returning to the ward after therapy to find a friend or friends waiting to see me — perhaps Chris and Terry or Tony, and sometimes some of my old mates, like Ossie and Whip.

Sitting in my chair one afternoon, I started thinking about when I was at home, and remembered how fed up I used to get with the day to day routine that my life was going through. Now I realised it did not matter what you did, if you had to do anything day in and day out it too would become routine. Although there wasn't much we could do to change the way our lives were going, we could do something about other things that got us down. Since I had been in Stoke Mandeville the meals had always been the same — the only difference being that Wednesday's dinner became Friday's tea and Thursday's tea became Monday's lunch and so on. Then, the following week the rota would be changed again. On several different occasions we tried to get a change to our regular diet by phoning the local Chinese takeaway, then phoning a taxi to pick our meal up for us and bring it to the ward. This was one of Frank's ideas, and I may add we used it more frequently as the months went on. Another way we got a variety in our diet was to get one of the voluntary girls who came to visit us on Wednesday evenings to call at the local fish and chip shop on her way to the hospital. This she did almost every Wednesday and so gave us a welcome change from macaroni cheese or Welsh rarebit and mashed potato.

Being able to get on with my therapy all week with very little interruption helped me no end. My swimming was gradually improving and I was now able to swim on my back using just my arms. I did this by holding them out to the side and pushing the water downwards towards my feet. After I had practised this I tried swimming on my front. This was slightly more difficult, as when I ran out of breath I had to raise my arm to attract the attention of the physiotherapist who was looking after me. If I thought no one had noticed I would be overcome with a terrible fear of drowning: the raising of the arm was an indication that I wanted to be turned over; I had not quite got the hang of turning myself over so that I could take in a deep breath. Over the weeks I spent in the pool I think I must have cost Aylesbury Water Board quite a bit of money with all the water I consumed during my weekly visits.

Not only was my swimming improving, my archery was too. I had now made such progress that Peter asked if I would like to come later in the afternoon when there would only be two or three others there who were paraplegics and who did not need bandaging like me. I had always liked sport of one kind or another and archery had given me the chance to compete in that field once again. Stoke Mandeville was well known all over the world for its expertise in caring for the spinally injured, and there wasn't a day went by without a group of new students, either from this country or abroad, visiting the different departments. It was more by Peter's judgement than luck that they would always turn up at the archery class when I was there. Having me there gave him the opportunity to show the students the difference between paraplegics (those who had broken their backs) and tetraplegics like myself (those with broken necks) by seeing them compete against one another. He managed to arrange a demonstration almost every day, and by the time I came to leave the hospital I knew his speech off by heart.

September was drawing on and summer was coming to a close. Although on most days I could still get away with just wearing a T-shirt which made dressing comparatively easy, I still needed considerable help in that area. I could get my T-shirt on by myself and I could pull up my jeans once they had been pulled over my knees. But shoes and socks — well they were still a non-starter as far as I was concerned! So the mornings that I wasn't swimming were taken up by going up to the Occupational Therapy department where I would dress and undress several times, trying to overcome the many difficulties that faced me. As the days passed I slowly improved and so began to dress as much as I could in the ward. Unfortunately, though, I still had to have the lower part of my body washed for me. That is until Lawrence suggested that if I sat up and he brought a bowl to me, I could wash my private parts and then dress my lower half before getting into my wheelchair and going to the ward bathroom to wash my face and hands and brush my teeth. This I began to do and for the first time I was glad that I was woken earlier in the mornings because washing and dressing took so much longer than it had once done.

I had overcome my feeding problems and now, after many trials and tribulations, had almost overcome the dressing problems too. The only trouble with dressing myself was that it was ten o'clockish before I was ready to leave the ward to go to occupational therapy — to learn to do something else. I was being taught how to type with two fingers, the index one on each hand. This I achieved quite well, and went on to learn the correct procedure for setting out a letter etc. I enjoyed typing as this was one way of writing a letter to Kate, saying the things I wanted to say that I couldn't have done on the phone in a ward full of people. Not only that, but it was also good therapy for my fingers — albeit just the two of them. Another thing I now had time to have a go at was washing my hair with the aid of one of those shower things that you fit onto the taps. I had several attempts at it, and learnt that one of the things to avoid was getting shampoo onto the bottle as it made it very slippery to hold while I tried to pour some into my other hand. Also, I learnt not to have the water coming out of the shower too fast, because if I did I would not only wash my hair but also my back, stomach, trousers and anybody or thing that was close to me. Again, I found with each time I had a go I became better and better, and so once again achieved something else that I had desperately wanted to do while I had been lying in bed all those weeks after my accident.

As I said before, occupational therapy and swimming took all the morning, but as I was improving in these, so I was also improving in physiotherapy in the afternoons. After finishing lunch all of us in wheelchairs would disappear to the different departments. I had to make my way down to the department past the canteen. Once there I would do a stint on the mats, then it was into my chair and onto the next thing; learning to transfer myself from the chair onto a bed or into a chair and then back into my wheelchair again. I did this in the following way: first I would wheel myself up close to the bed or bench or whatever I was transferring onto, then I would take hold of the leg nearest to the bed from behind the knee and lift it over and onto the bed, then do the same with the other leg, after that it was a case of edging myself forward in my chair, putting one hand onto the bed and the other onto the chair and then lifting my whole body up and over. You would be surprised how much strength you need to do this: not only do you need the strength to lift yourself over, but once there you have to have enough strength to get back again. It wasn't something you did once and then it was mastered, you had to do it time and time again to gain confidence and feel that you were not going to fall forward out of the chair and onto the floor, or get half-way across and have your arms give out and find yourself stranded between bed and chair. I would attempt everything that Jane asked me. This was because I had complete confidence in her, and also because I knew she wouldn't ask me to do anything that she thought or knew I wouldn't be able to do.

All these things I did in therapy, like the rolling on the mat, or the transfers and the pulleys, were helping me to overcome the difficulties of doing everyday things, so I worked at them harder and harder each day. On most days I would end up competing with Keith on the two sets of pulleys, although he was pulling much heavier weights than me. He would start off by doing ten or fifteen pulls with both arms, then it would be my turn and I would have to match whatever he had done. By the time I had finished my fifteen pulls he would start again and this is how it went on until one of us gave up through sheer agony in our arms.

Having Keith there pushing me to my limit gave me the chance to have a go on the parallel bars which was quite unusual for a tetraplegic. First I had to get used to standing up again. This was achieved by using a standing frame: it was a large wooden, stationary frame that you wheeled yourself into: once in you took the footplates off your wheelchair, then placed your feet in front of a strap on the frame to prevent them shooting back. There was another strap a little higher up which your knees rested against; a little higher up still was a sort of desk top. Once you were up onto your feet you lay across until, in my case, Jane came and did up the final strap which went across your bottom and held you in. Then it was just a matter of pushing yourself up and there you were, standing on your own two feet again. And here I was, standing up for the first time in almost five months.

As I stood there I felt a warm glow all over my face and felt this tingling sensation in my toes and feet. I looked across the physio department and it seemed as if a cloud of mist had drifted into the room and was surrounding everything I tried to focus on. Then I was fighting for breath. It was at this point that I realised what was happening and remembered when it had happened before: it had been exactly the same when I first began to sit up, and again when I first got out of bed and into my wheelchair. Jane was standing beside me and must have seen the blood drain from my face. 'OK, Andy. Take some deep breaths,' she said.

I did as she said, but even the sound in the room seemed to drift away and her voice was no louder than a whisper.

'OK, Andy. Lie forward over this.' She put a pillow over the desk top. There I was, still on my feet but bent at the waist lying on this pillow, looking at the floor beneath me.

'Keep breathing deeply,' I heard Jane saying and I did as I was told. Soon the mist in front of my eyes began to subside and I could once again focus with them. At last I felt I could say something. 'Crumbs, Jane, I thought I was going to pass out then.'

Jane explained that everyone felt like that at first because it is a shock to the heart suddenly, after months of either lying down or sitting up, to find it's got to start pumping blood all round the body in a vertical position rather than a horizontal one. It was like asking it to push blood up Mount Everest instead of along the flat roads of Holland. I kept breathing in deeply until I heard Jane say, 'Now, how about having another go?' I wasn't sure but I also knew that I'd got to overcome this if I was going to get onto those parallel bars.

'OK, Jane,' I said, and with that I pushed up onto my arms once more, breathing in deeply through my mouth. I found I could stand there much longer, until the mist once again began to fall down in front of my eyes. After the second attempt Jane unbuckled me and let me sit down in my chair. 'Oh,' I thought to myself, 'I've blown my chances of going on the bars.' Jane put my footplates back on, then lifted my feet onto them. 'You have done very well for your first attempt,' she said.

'Oh thanks, Jane,' I said. 'I thought I had blown my chance of going onto the bars.'

'No, don't worry, I will have you up on those bars all right, just give yourself time. Now you had better get a move on or you will be late for your archery class.' As I pushed myself up the corridor I had this lovely warm feeling inside — I suppose of self satisfaction. I was on a kind of high for the first time in months.

Just as things were beginning to move for me in one sense, so Mum and Dad had had to do some moving of their own. As I would no longer be able to get up the stairs, they were told that they would have to move from our house into a bungalow before it would be possible for me to come home. They had bought a bungalow, moved in and settled in well. As they were describing it to me, I realised where it was: not far from the first house that we lived in on Palfry Heights: in fact it was just down the road on the next estate. The only difference was that this estate was all private houses rather than council houses. I knew exactly where the house was as I had had a paper round there from the age of about thirteen to sixteen. I thought of the place and different memories flashed through my mind: how when work first started there we used to play on the large mounds of earth that had been created by the work of the bulldozers; or how when the houses were being built we used to jump off the scaffolding into a pile of sand; then I remembered how, when I was about thirteen, there was a night I lost my virginity (if that's the word) with a girl the same age as myself in one of the new garages just around the corner where my new home would now be; then, finally, my last memory was of a time when I was about fifteen and I used to meet a girl who was doing a paper round also. As our rounds crossed I'd stop and chat to her and after we had both finished we would slide off somewhere for half an hour before going our separate ways again. As these different memories flashed through my mind they brought both joy and sorrow. There was, as always, the joy of thinking back to fond memories, but the sadness too because I wondered if they would be the last fond memories that I would have.

Chapter 13
Weekend at Home

It was Monday, the day for doctors' rounds, but now that I was in my chair I had to line up outside the office and wait until it was my turn to go in. There were two or three before me, then it was my turn. I pushed myself in and the door closed behind me. There they all sat: Dr Silver, Dr Bash, Head of Occupational Therapy, Head of Physiotherapy, Sister Shilton. Then Dr Silver said his now immortalised words, 'Well, how are you today, Andrew?'

'Oh, I'm fine, thanks,' I replied, and he began to ask the others questions. First: 'Dr Bash, how is his bladder? No problems there?'

'No,' Dr Bash replied.

Then Dr Silver moved on to occupational therapy. 'How is he getting on there? Can he dress himself and wash, etc?'

'Yes, he is doing very well, although he still needs a bit of help with his dressing.'

'Next one, please,' I thought to myself, 'here it comes — physiotherapy.'

'How is he doing there? Can he transfer himself say onto the bed or toilet, etc?'

'Well, he is getting there but he still needs some help, though,' and there I had been, thinking I was doing well.

I found I was saying to myself, 'Your turn, sister.'

'How long has he been here now, sister?'

'Well, it's nearly five months,' she replied.

Here comes the big summary I thought: 'Was I right or was I right?'

'Well, what do you think? Do you think he is ready to go home for a weekend?'

Sorry, what was that? Was I hearing things? No, I wasn't, as each in turn said they thought that there was no reason why I should not go home this coming weekend.

'Is that all right with you, Andrew?'

'Yer, thanks,' I replied.

'Your father will have to come up on Thursday so we can show him what he has to do for you. Is that all right? Then you can go home on Friday afternoon and come back on Sunday afternoon. Sister, will you ring his father and make the arrangements?'

The door was opened and I wheeled myself out and down the ward a short way, where I sat trying to take in what had just been said. It was strange. I sat there in two frames of mind: one, pleased at the thought of going home, the other, frightened at how I was going to cope with being away from the hospital for the first time.

It was Monday, as I have said, and our ward's day for the mobile phone. As I sat in my chair contemplating the thought of going home I could hear it ringing at the far end of the ward. It was still only around nine o'clock and I remember thinking, 'Crumbs, someone's pretty keen.' The phone was continually used during the evening but very rarely would it ring at this hour of the morning. It stopped ringing and some instinct told me at the very moment that Marcia called out, 'Andy, it's for you, one of your girl-friends, I think.'

'Hello, who is that?' I asked.

'It's Jane,' came the reply. It was Kim's girlfriend — 'What was she doing ringing me,' I thought. She had always written before.

'I thought you would probably want cheering up, seeing that your mum was having her operation today. She must have had it by now,' she ended. It was just like it had been ten minutes earlier when I had heard the news about going home. I heard the words spoken but could not take them in.

'Sorry, Jane, what did you say?' I replied.

She must have noticed the astonishment in my voice at the news she had just given me. 'Oh, I am sorry, Andy, I didn't realise you knew nothing about it.' As she tried to apologise for letting the cat out of the bag, words of sympathy came from her end of the telephone such as, 'There's no need to worry, it's only a small operation,' and the other one that sticks in my mind was, 'loads of women have to have an operation like this. It's nothing to worry about.' My family, in a moment of wisdom, had decided to keep the fact of Mum's operation a secret from me as they thought it would cause me unnecessary concern, but looking back I think I would have preferred to have known rather than find out the way I did. Anyway, never mind, after replacing the receiver of the telephone I found I could not quite grasp what had happened to me that morning: first the news of going home for a weekend had come as a complete surprise but a nice one, then this shock was the complete opposite. Mum was having an operation — to put a name to it, a hysterectomy. I learnt later that it entailed taking away the womb and ovaries to cure the heavy bleeding that some women suffer at the given time of each month. Mum had suffered with this for the last couple of years and, although often very ill with it, had never let it stop her from being the wonderful mother and wife that she was and still is.

I worried all through the day and was unable to concentrate on my physiotherapy and archery. I wheeled myself down to the bottom of the ward and as I looked out of the French doors and across the grounds I prayed to God that he would take care of her and bring her through the operation safely. That night I phoned home and my first words were: 'How's Mum? Is she OK?' Dad assured me that she was and then asked how I had found out. I told him Jane had rung me that morning, not knowing that I didn't know anything about it. He told me that they thought I would only worry and that's why they had decided not tell me. We chatted a while and he told me that the sister had contacted him about me coming home that weekend. 'Andy, I think we had better make it the following weekend, that way you can visit Mum while she is convalescing.' I knew that what he was saying made sense and so agreed. Our family, which had had no cause to call upon the National Health Service except when the new additions to the family arrived, now found two of us in their capable hands, first myself and now my mum.

I phoned every night, keeping a check on how Mum was doing, but during the day I was working hard on trying to improve myself before the weekend arrived. Before I could go home there was something else I would have to learn to do, to get from my wheelchair into a car. The procedure for this was as follows: I had to wheel myself up as close to the passenger seat as possible, then lift my legs into the front well of the car and then, using a special shiny-surfaced board, cross from my chair into the front seat of the car. It all sounds simple but it took quite a lot of effort on my behalf. Anyway, Jane helped me practise it each day in the car park. Then on Thursday my brother-in-law, John, and his father arrived to see me. Just as I was passing the canteen I saw them coming towards me.

'Hello, John and Les. What a nice surprise!' I said as they reached me. John suggested we go to the canteen for a drink. 'OK, but I can't be long as I have got my archery class to go to.'

We went in and had a quick coffee and then John pushed me along the corridor while Les walked beside me. As we went into the hall I asked Peter if it would be all right for John and Les to stay and watch. He said it would, but he had a group of students coming in later from Sweden. Peter began to bandage me up and at the same time he chatted away to John and Les. Once I was ready he pushed me over to the line I fired from. After firing a couple of rounds of arrows, in came the students Peter had told us about. With their arrival, John offered to collect the arrows for me and the other lad who was doing archery with me. Peter accepted his help and began his now familiar speech as I fired my arrows and John retrieved them. Les, in the meantime, was taking in everything that Peter said. Then the next thing we knew he was answering all the questions that Peter was asking the students and nodding his head in agreement with everything he said. John and I watched in amazement, until we could not restrain ourselves any longer and began to cry with laughter. You had to be there to appreciate it: there was Les amongst all these students beating them to the answers to the questions! It was beautiful!

After finishing archery John pushed me back to the ward and we were still laughing at what had just taken place.

After we'd had a cup of tea, Jane appeared in the ward and suggested that perhaps John could take me out for a short trip in his car so I could get used to travelling at speed before the following weekend. John took me across to the car and helped me in with the use of the shiny board. Once in, he fastened my seat belt for me and then, putting the car in gear, pulled away very slowly. It was a weird experience at first: it seemed as if I was going much faster than I was. We drove through the gates and turned left. It was the first time that I had been out of the grounds of the hospital. We did what I suppose you would call a trip round the block, just touching the outskirts of the town. The other strange thing I found as we drove along was that when John put his foot on the brake, I felt myself leaning forward, unable to stop myself. But, all said and done, it was much better than I thought it was going to be. We turned back into the hospital gates and a few minutes later John was helping me out of the car. I had overcome another hurdle and was glad that I had had the chance of getting used to travelling in a car before the three hour journey I would be going on the next weekend.

Jo and Tim arrived to see me on Saturday and brought a surprise present with them. It was my own pool cue, a two piece one with the top part fitting inside the bottom; it was also carved all round the shaft where you gripped. All in all a very posh looking thing. The final touch was that when you were not using it, it doubled as a walking stick. 'We knew you liked them, so we bought it for you knowing it would come in handy later on,' Jo said. Before my accident, John, the landlord of The Grange, had been selling them but at that time there was no way I could have afforded to buy one. I thanked them both very much and, although I didn't say much, was choked by their generosity. They stayed with me all afternoon just sitting and chatting. They had been so good to me all through the time since the accident, visiting me almost every week, making sure there was nothing I needed and so on. After they left that evening I asked one of the orderlies to put my cue together for me and, as I fumbled with it in my hands, my eyes filled with tears as I thought about the times when I played pool at The Grange, and of the laughs I had with my mates.

Kate arrived to see me on Sunday with Chris, Terry, Jackie and Darren and during the afternoon we all went down to the canteen for a cup of tea. While we were sitting there I asked Kate if she would light a cigarette for me as there was no way I could nip a match between my thumb and forefinger. It was then that Terry asked me to have a go at lighting his lighter. It was an electronic one which needed very little pressure on the switch to make it light. I fumbled with it until I finally got it to light. 'You can have it, Andy, that way you won't have to keep on asking people to light your cigarettes for you.' I didn't know what to say at first, then tried to refuse his generous offer, but Terry was having none of it. I thanked him very much for his kindness. This was the second time in two days that someone had done something for me, and again I was touched by such generosity. After finishing our tea we returned to the ward and sat around my bed talking. I know it must sound a bit repetitive when I say we sat around my bed talking, but there wasn't much else I could do. We couldn't all get out on the front grass and have a game of football or go into Aylesbury and try out the night life. No, sitting and talking about what had been going on in Brantham, or what I'd been up to in the week was about it really.

I loved them, though, for coming all that way to spend the afternoon with me and after they had gone always felt a kind of loss. Kate was still staying over at her relations until the next day when her mum came to pick her up. They stayed with me until late into the afternoon and Kate said how much she was looking forward to not having to make the long journey to Stoke Mandeville the following weekend. After they left that night I sat near my bed, listening to a favourite tape, and subsided into deep thought, asking myself the same sort of questions that I always did. 'Why me? Why should I be in this wheelchair? I know I was a bit of a lad but I was no worse than anyone else. Why should you choose me to suffer in this way, dear Lord? What dreadful thing did I do to make you put me in this wheelchair?' Then I would recall all the things that were not quite pure and white that I had done during my seventeen years on this earth and wondered if it was for this one or that one that I was now being punished. I would keep this up until I had narrowed it down to a couple of possibilities — because I had hurt someone in some way or because I had screwed around before getting married. Perhaps it was because I had caused Mum and Dad lots of worry by getting into trouble with the police at different times. This is how I would carry on until I finally dropped off to sleep.

The next couple of days passed quickly and it was soon Thursday afternoon. I had just finished my therapy and was returning to the ward when I met Dad in the corridor.

'Hi, Dad. You got here all right, then?' I asked. 'Where are you staying?'

'Oh, I am staying in the hostel just across the way,' he replied. It was a new situation for me and Dad. We loved each other as father and son but had never been that close. Dad, having always done shiftwork all his life, seemed to be at work more than he was at home. He had been a good father, though, and had always given all of us whatever we wanted material-wise, but I think he found it very hard to show his emotions. There were times when I was young when I would go to him for help with my reading, and at first he would sit and help me then, if I got stuck on a word or two, instead of calmly explaining it to me he would start to get agitated. There were other things: for instance, when I got older I wanted to do things with my dad as my mates were doing with theirs, such as going to football matches together or sharing some kind of hobby. I remember Dad taking me fishing. He sat me on one of those jetties, then helped me to set my rod up. Once I was set up, instead of sitting with me he moved down the bank and fished from there. Don't get me wrong! It wasn't all Dad's fault. I was just as much to blame. I think I went wrong by not going to him when I was worried about something. I was afraid he would think I was stupid. Then, as I grew older, I became overshadowed by my older sister, Jo. She was much brighter than me and whenever I made a contribution to the conversation she politely told me I was thick and that I didn't know anything. Then my younger sister, Lou, was born and with her arrival my avenue of love and understanding from my mum was cut off because she had to give most of her time and encouragement to Lou. I think this is why I withdrew into myself. I suppose the reason why I rebelled against everything was because I kept my thoughts and problems to myself all the time. Then there was the Law, the Establishment. Although the scrapes I got into were not serious, it was as if I was shouting, 'Look, I'm still here!' When I was at school I never tried as hard as I could have done, knowing that getting a bad report would get more of a reaction from Mum and Dad than a good one would have done. But now, looking back, I regret not having gone to Dad for help; I regret not having tried harder at school and so on. Having said that, though, I think my stubbornness helped me to cope as well as I was doing with this new problem in my life. If I hadn't been used to coping on my own, I wouldn't have been bloody-minded enough to say to myself, 'Well, I am going to walk again, even if it takes the rest of my life.'

Dad sat with me, Keith and Frank in the ward until quite late in the evening. We had a few games of cards and chatted about this and that. Then, when I was put to bed, Dad had to watch and see how to lift me into bed and how to help me undress. Afterwards he sat by my bed a bit longer until the lights were switched out and then left to go across to his room in the hostel. The following morning he arrived early to see how he had to help me on the loo. Once this was sorted out the sister took him into her office and gave him all the medical supplies that I would need for the weekend. After Sister had finished with him we popped down to the physio room where Jane showed him how to help me transfer from one thing to another. After that we returned to the ward. By this time it was lunch time, so Dad put my case and the rest of the things I would need in the car. I said goodbye to the lads in the ward as I pushed myself through the ward and reminded them that I would be back on Sunday. As I reached the sister's office she called to me, 'Off you go then, Andy. There is nothing to worry about. You have got everything you need and we will see you on Sunday!' I said goodbye and Dad pushed me along to the car.

It was a warm day, I thought, as I transferred to the car. Dad put my chair into the back of the car then, after putting my seatbelt on, started her up and turned out of the car park and began to travel up the long drive to the main gates. As we turned onto the main road my heart began to beat faster and inwardly I was trembling like a leaf. Dad asked if I was OK and I replied I was. As we got going I seemed to relax a bit, but everything looked as if it was going much faster than

I remembered: the traffic coming towards us, the houses and trees somehow passed that much quicker; but all these things did not worry me that much. As we passed through towns, with the inevitable stopping and starting at traffic lights, I began to start getting jittery again, although even that didn't compare to the way I felt when we got behind a large lorry: overtaking them did not bother me, but if the traffic slowed down and we were directly behind one and all I could see was its rear lights and huge back doors towering down on me, it was then I really started to panic. I would have to close my eyes and breathe in deeply to try and subside the fear I felt inside. However, once we were able to pull out and pass the lorry I would relax again until the next time.

We had been travelling for about an hour or so when Dad pulled into a lay-by so that we could have a drink of tea from the flask which he had had filled at the canteen before we left. He had already stopped several times before so that I could lift myself up on my arms and give my backside some relief. I had to do this continually whether I was sitting in my chair or in the car: it was to prevent the pressure being concentrated in one place and so stop me from getting pressure sores. We finished our tea and then started on our way again. I think it was after about two hours in the car and when he had passed the fifth or sixth town that I began to realise what an awful long journey it had been for the people who had regularly come to visit me, and why it had taken so much out of Dad in those first two weeks when he had repeatedly done this journey, there and back, each day. Another half an hour passed and we joined a road that I knew: the A12.

'Not much further now, Andy,' Dad said, and as the familiar names of the small villages flashed past I knew we would soon be turning off the busy A12 and into the village of East Bergholt. As we drove down the village street and past the church I was consciously looking for any changes that might have taken place during my five months in hospital. But I could see no change: it was as if I had never been away. We left Bergholt and reached Brantham. Then we were driving into the new estate that my home was now on. Dad pulled up outside the bungalow. 'There you go, Andy. Welcome Home,' he said. Jo and Lou must have been looking out for us as no sooner had the car stopped than they were opening the door for me and with big smiles over their faces welcoming me home.

Dad helped me out of the car while Jo and Lou carried the things in from the back. As Dad pushed me down the path to the front door I commented on the ramp which led up to it. 'Oh me and Terry fixed that up a couple of days ago,' he answered. As Dad pushed me into the living room I looked all round me — at the three piece suite, the wall unit and so on, but although these were all familiar things it looked different. The paint on the walls and the carpet on the floor were not the same as the ones I had pictured in my mind so many times in the last five months. The shapes of the rooms themselves were all different. This was now my home but to me home was the house that I had left on that Friday morning five months ago. Jo cooked tea that evening and although they were all trying to make me feel at home I missed the presence of Mum and the warmth and re-assurance that only she could give. After tea Kate arrived and spent the whole evening with me. We went into my bedroom and for the first time in months were able to kiss and hold one another. I had brought my radio cassette home with me and we listened to tapes and talked until it was time for her to leave. Dad helped me to bed that night and also set the alarm clock to wake him during the night so that he could come in and turn me.

'Are you OK, Andy?' he said, as he checked to make sure I was lying correctly on the pillows on my bed.

'Yer, I am fine, thanks, Dad,' I replied. Now that I was settled in bed first Jo, then Lou came in and said goodnight to me, then they switched off the light and closed my door. As I lay there, with a light shining into my bedroom from the streetlight outside I had time to think. 'I'm home,' I said to myself, but it then dawned upon me that nothing had changed: just because I was home there hadn't been some incredible miracle; I hadn't been made well simply because I was home. As I lay there thinking that this was how it was going to be for the rest of my life tears slowly filled my eyes until there was nowhere else for them to go but to run from the corners down my cheeks. I lifted my arm from under the sheets and as I wiped my eyes began to think of times past, the happy memories that I held close to my heart. As the different memories filled my mind the unhappiness that I had felt minutes earlier slowly drifted away until I too drifted, not away, but into a deep sleep.

Saturday morning. Dad helped me to wash and dress and also gave me a hand with transferring from my bed into my wheelchair. Jo and Lou waited until I came through before having their breakfast. We all sat round the kitchen table eating cereals and they asked me whether I had slept all right and I said I had. After breakfast I wheeled myself into the lounge. I was sitting there reading the paper and smoking a cigarette when the first of my visitors arrived: it was my sister, Judy, her husband, John, and their two children, Lorna and Marcus. They sat down and their first question was: 'What's it like to be back home, then? Great, I reckon.' They were not the first to ask and answer that question that day. They had only been there a short while when my other sister, Brenda, and her husband, Dave, and their two children arrived. It was the first time I had seen Brenda since my accident and as she bent over and kissed me I thanked her for sending me the letters and postcards that she had done every week for the last umpteen weeks. It was the first time that Brenda's kids, Craig and Amanda, had seen me since my accident and not without cause, they were a little bit wary of my wheelchair. All four kids were a bit shy and, although I tried to understand, I couldn't help feeling a bit hurt. Looking back now I can understand what a shock it must have been for them. They all stayed until midday then left so Jo could dish up dinner. 'It's your favourite,' she said as she arranged my food on the plate, and she was right: eggs, beans, bacon and chips were my favourite.

That afternoon I had more visitors: my dear friends, Chris, Terry, their daughter, Jackie, and son, Darren. They stayed chatting all afternoon and also remarked how nice it was only having to come half a mile to visit me rather than a hundred or so. During the afternoon Terry offered to come back with me and Dad when I returned to Stoke Mandeville the following day and give Dad a break from the driving. Dad gratefully accepted his offer, but said that he was going to take me to see Mum on the way. After Chris and Terry had left we had tea. Kate arrived again for the evening, but instead of going home she stayed overnight — unfortunately for me, not in the same bed. Thinking back again it would have probably been the wrong time to try and prove my manhood as I undoubtedly would have failed.

By the time I was washed and dressed on Sunday a good part of the morning had already passed. Dad, Lou, Kate and I spent the rest of the morning sitting in the lounge while Jo cooked the lunch. After eating roast beef and all the trimmings Dad packed all my things in the car and then it was my turn. As he pushed me up the path towards the car, Terry arrived. Dad, Terry, Lou and Kate were coming on the journey back to the hospital. With the help of my shiny board I slid into the front passenger seat while Terry, Lou and Kate got into the back. Dad put my chair in the boot, then got in the driver's seat. As he was about to pull away Judy and John arrived to say goodbye. After saying my goodbyes to them and Jo from the front of the car, Dad pulled away and we were on our way.

The convalescent home where Mum was recuperating was on the same side of Colchester as Brantham so there was no need to go through the shopping area of the town. As we pulled into the grounds I could see the beds through the windows. We drove past to get to the car park. Dad stopped the car then helped me into my chair again. Once settled,

Kate pushed me back into the home. It felt strange going into a kind of hospital to visit Mum when the shoe had been on the other foot, so to speak, for the last five months. As I turned into the small ward I saw her sitting on her bed. Her eyes caught sight of me and a huge smile came onto her face and, as I reached her bed, she began to cry.

'Oh what a lovely surprise. I didn't expect to see you, love,' she said.

'I didn't know the sight of me made people cry,' I replied jokingly.

'It's just that I'm so pleased to see you.' She wiped the tears from her eyes and I asked how she was feeling now.

'Oh I am getting on fine,' was her answer.

As the others pulled up chairs and sat down beside her bed I looked around, taking in all that I saw. Then, in turn, the others asked her the usual questions: what had she had for lunch; did she sleep well last night; had she got everything she needed and so on. Then Mum asked me how I enjoyed my first weekend at home and told me how she had wanted so much to be there when I arrived. I told her that it had been OK, and said how I wished she would have been there as well. We carried on chatting to one another until the bell went for the end of visiting time. Mum got off her bed and kissed me goodbye and as I smiled and turned to go out of the door it felt strange to be the one who was leaving rather than the one being left behind. We all got back into the car and as we drove past the window of Mum's ward Dad slowed down so that I could wave at her. Then we were out of the gates and on our way again. I remember thinking as we travelled along how I had felt each time my visitors had left me and knew exactly what Mum was going through at this moment.

Chapter 14
Why Me?

After almost three hours in the car we were about to turn into the gates of Stoke Mandeville hospital. We had stopped several times along the road so that I could relieve the pressure on my backside. We had also stopped for a bite to eat at a Little Chef. Dad, Terry and Lou went in while Kate and I stayed in the car. I didn't fancy going through all the palava of getting in and out of my wheelchair again and also wasn't ready to face people staring at me because I was in a wheelchair. It was almost a relief to be back into the comfortable surroundings of the hospital where people in wheelchairs were commonplace and where people thought nothing of it. Dad pushed me along the corridor and back to the ward while Kate, Terry and Lou brought all my things. As I passed the lads in bed at the top of the ward, Max, Dave and Tommy called out, welcoming me back and asking how I had enjoyed my weekend at home. I told them that it had been OK but that I had missed them so much I couldn't wait to get back (at the same time I had a big grin on my face). Keith had also been home for a weekend and as we passed him to get to my bed I asked him how he had got on.

'Not too bad, and you?'

'Yer, OK.'

Dad placed my things on my bed. By this time it was nearly half past seven and as I looked at Dad I could see he was very tired.

'Bet you're glad Terry's driving back, Dad,' I said.

'Yes, I am. I don't think I could face driving all that way back again tonight,' he replied.

They sat with me till about eight then Terry said, 'We'd better make a move if we are going to get home tonight.'

As I said goodbye I thanked Dad for his help over the weekend and then thanked Terry for coming with us and giving Dad a rest from the driving. Dad and Terry said goodbye, then Lou kissed me on the cheek and walked up the ward with them while I said goodbye to Kate. She bent down and kissed me and as she did I touched her cheek with my hand. Then she laid her head on my shoulders and I whispered, 'Oh darling, I do love you.'

'And I love you too, Andy, and always will. There will never be anyone else for me but you,' she said as she straightened up. 'I'll write and phone during the week and see you on Sunday, OK?'

'Ok, babe,' I replied, then watched as she walked to the end of the ward and waved as she turned out of the door. Then I pushed myself over to the French doors and watched as they got into the car and drove up the drive and out of the main gates, waving until they were out of sight.

My bottom felt very sore from sitting all day so now that they had gone I asked the orderlies if they would put me to bed. As I lay there Keith came over. 'How did it really go, Andy?' he said.

'You know, so-so. My dad and sisters and that were great, but I could tell they were choosing their words carefully so as not to say anything that might upset me. I hated the fact that Dad had to help me wash and that; you know, being in here you think nothing of the nurses and orderlies helping you, but when it's your dad, well that's something else.'

'Yer, I know how you feel. It's like when Dad carries me upstairs to the loo in his arms. You know, I feel so useless and that inside I want to explode. This was my third weekend home and some of my relatives came round with their young kids. I was sitting in the living room when one of them just turned to me and said ''You're a cripple, aren't you?'' I know he is only young and that, but it really hit home and I couldn't stop myself from exploding. I said, ''Get him out of here,'' and just went bloody wild. Then I sat there and cried my eyes out.'

'Oh crumbs, Keith, that must have been hard. I don't know how I would have reacted if it had happened to me. I think I would have been just like you.'

Keith sat near my bed and we carried on talking until eleven had turned. We had become quite good mates over the last two or three months. He was just twenty-one and came from Watford. To look at him he was very much like Rod Stewart, and having talked about our pasts together I knew he had been as much of a lad as I had. It wasn't until a couple of days later that I found that he had taken the incident at the weekend much harder than he had let on, and his mum and dad were very worried about the threat he had made to take his own life. He had seemed quiet since our chat on Sunday night, but as the week drew on was putting more and more effort into his therapy as if to prove his young nephew wrong.

Just because I had been home for one weekend did not mean I would go automatically every weekend but only when it was possible for my dad to be there to help me. Because of him working shifts he might be on nights and then there would be no one to help me turn in the night. More than a week had gone by since my trip home and I was back into the routine of swimming, archery, occupational and physio therapy, but going home had shown me just how much harder I had got to work and improve if I was to do the things that I had dreamed about since my accident. Knowing what I had to do spurred me on to try harder at everything I did, especially the different therapies. When Jane asked if I had had enough on the mat or in the pool I asked if I could stay on or in a bit longer. When Keith and I were doing our pulleys together I would not give in to the nagging pains in my arms until the last possible moment, and when I was standing up in my frame I forced myself to overcome the feeling of faintness. Slowly my efforts began to pay off: it was much easier to push my wheelchair and to transfer from one thing to another and I was beginning to overcome the many difficulties involved in dressing.

It was Wednesday afternoon. I had just finished my physiotherapy and was setting off to go up to archery when Jane said, 'Oh Andy, after you have finished archery and been back to the ward, stay there and I will pick you up and bring you back down here and make your plaster casts for you.'

'You mean for my legs, so I can have a go in the parallel bars?'

'Yes, that's right. So stay in the ward and I will pick you up at half three.'

As I pushed myself to archery I felt really great. 'I am going to have a go at least, then,' I kept saying to myself.

After tea I did as I was told and waited until Jane arrived. She pushed me back to the therapy department, then helped me onto a bench-type bed and after taking my trousers, socks and shoes off, turned me over onto my stomach. She began cutting strips of cloth plaster and laying them on my legs. When she knew she had got enough she poured water over them and started to mould them to my legs. The casts started from almost the top of my thigh and finished just above my ankle. Jane added a few more strips of plaster, then a bit more water, and then she had finished. 'I have got to leave them on a little while so I can mould them a bit more as they dry out,' she said. She left them on for several minutes and then, once she was happy with them, removed them and laid them to one side to dry out completely. With her help I dressed myself again and transferred to my wheelchair.

'When will I be able to use them, Jane?' I asked.

'Oh, not for several days,' she replied. As she pushed me back to the ward I asked why I had to wait so long. 'Well if they are not dried out completely the first time you use them they will crack.'

'All right then, Jane, I think I can hang on a couple more days.'

Once back in the ward Jane left to visit one of her other patients while I sat turning over in my mind the thought of finally getting up into those parallel bars.

That night I played cards with Frank and Keith at one of the large green tables at the bottom of the ward. As I could not hold seven or eight cards at one time I would lay them on my lap and as the table was fairly high it would shield them from both Keith and Frank. The only trouble with laying them on my lap was that I often knocked one onto the floor, but as long as the little wheels on my chair were pointing forward I was quite safe to lean over and pick it up. Tonight, however, I forgot to check and as I leant forward under the table my chair tipped up and I felt myself going forward but was unable to stop myself. My natural instinct, however, came into play and I shot my arms out in front of me to stop my head hitting the tiled floor. There I was in a heap on the floor under the table. At almost the same moment both Keith and Frank's heads appeared under the table and, once they saw I was OK, they burst into uncontrollable laughter. Lawrence and Nicky came to my rescue and once they had lifted me back into my chair and checked to see that I hadn't broken anything they also began to laugh at my expense. I could see the funny side of it, but at the same time it had shaken me up because it was the first time I had fallen out of my chair. I played a few more hands of cards, then asked to be put to bed.

As I lay there, I thought about my eventful day. It seemed that no sooner did I think I was improving in one way or another when something else would happen to show me how much more I had got to do to achieve my ambitions. It had been the same at the weekend: the joy of going home, then the stark reality of how little I could actually do for myself. Then today the excitement of finally getting my plaster casts made, then bang! — I couldn't even stop myself from falling forwards. 'Why do I go on?' I asked myself. 'Why? Because I want to walk again, that's why.'

Thursday and Friday slipped by and now the weekend had come once again. This weekend I would be staying at the hospital and my family and friends would again have to make the long journey to visit me. Saturday mornings were taken up picking out my horses in the races that were to be shown on the television that afternoon. It had been several weeks earlier when I was still in bed that Keith had introduced me to the pastime of backing horses. He had found out about one of the orderlies who would take our bets down to the local bookies and who would also collect our winnings if we had been lucky. I had finished my lunch and was waiting for the horse racing to start when who should appear but my sister, Jo.

'What are you doing here? Where is Tim?' I asked.

'I knew you were on your own and Fred didn't want to come so I came on my own.'

(Just in case you are wondering, Tim and Fred are the same person. Tim was his real name and Fred his nickname.) It was a big surprise to see Jo on her own as it had only been a matter of days since she had passed her driving test.

'You must have been nervous coming all this way on your own,' I said.

'You're telling me. At one point I didn't know whether to carry on or turn round and go back, but I decided to keep coming and here I am.'

We sat and chatted and she told me all that was happening back home. 'Mum will be coming home sometime this week,' she told me. We went down to the canteen for a cup of tea, and stayed there for some time. Then, as she pushed me back to the ward, she said Dad would be coming up the following Friday to bring me home for another weekend. 'Mum should also be at home by then,' she said.

We turned into the ward, and sat near my bed talking away until I realised how late it was getting. 'Jo, I don't want to get rid of you but I am worried about you driving home when it is dark, especially on roads you don't know very well.'

'Yes, I think I had better make a move as it will be nine o'clock and more by the time I get home,' she replied.

'Thanks ever so much for coming, and you will take it easy on the way back, won't you? And promise to phone me the minute you get in?' I said.

'Yes, OK. I'm really glad I made the effort to come on my own,' she said as she walked to the door. I watched her get into her car and then waved as she drove past the ward and out of the main gates. I thought about her several times during the evening, until she finally phoned about nine o'clock. 'I'm home, Andy, and I will see you next weekend, OK?' I was pleased she had got home safely and was now able to relax and watch the telly.

Kate arrived on Sunday and stayed over until Monday. As usual, now that I was going home every other weekend I found that more and more time was being lost when I could have been getting therapy. On Tuesday I had my first opportunity to try out my plaster casts. I had done my usual stint of therapy straight after lunch then had gone off and done my archery. Instead of remaining in the ward after afternoon tea I returned to the therapy department just up from the ward.

'OK, Andy, are you fit, then?' Jane asked.

'Fit as I will ever be,' I replied.

Jane put me into the parallel bars then removed the footplates from my chair, at the same time straightening my legs out from the sitting position that they had been in over the last hour or so. Then she placed the plaster casts down the backs of my legs and fixed them with several bandages, making sure that they were nice and tight so that my knee joint could not bend. 'All right, Andy, I think we are ready.

Put your hands on either bar, now lean forward.' At this point Jane called another physiotherapist, Penny, over, to give her a hand. 'Penny, could you stand in front of him and when I pull him up, can you hold him there until I can get in behind him? Right, Andy, push up on the bars. That's it.'

As I pushed up Jane gave me a helping hand from the back and there I was standing on my own two feet held straight by the plaster casts. I felt Jane get behind me, then she pulled me straight so my weight was now on the backs of my feet and my hips were forced forwards. Once Penny could see that Jane had got hold of me she moved out from in front of me and I could now see myself in the large mirror that stretched the whole length of the wall. 'Breathe deeply, Andy, so that you don't feel faint,' Jane said.

I did as she said but at the same time stared at myself in the mirror. 'Was that really me standing there?' I asked myself. I tried to relax and get used to being up on my feet.

'OK, Andy, I think that will do for today.' Jane called Penny over to help me back into my chair. As I reached the chair I let the air from my lungs shoot out of my mouth in one huge sigh of relief.

'That was OK, Jane,' I said. 'It felt really great to be on my feet once again.'

'Yes,' she replied, 'you did well. Tomorrow we will see if you can take a couple of steps.'

'Steps? Hey, that can't be bad,' I thought and was now eagerly waiting for tomorrow to arrive.

It was now Wednesday afternoon. The morning had flown by, probably because I was so eager for the afternoon to arrive. After lunch I pushed myself down to the physio department as usual then, after finishing my stint on the mat and in the standing frame, pushed myself back up to archery. I must have been thinking ahead as my shooting was well off its usual standard. After finishing there it was back to the ward for a quick cup of tea, then on to the physio department just up from the ward. Once there, Jane fixed my casts on again and then, with the help of Penny, I was up on my two pins for the second time in two days. After standing there five minutes or so I became relaxed and felt capable of taking my first step in five, going on six months.

'OK, Andy, lean forward a bit; now push up on your arms, lift your feet up and place them forward of you just a few inches; now push your hips forward again and straighten up.'

I pushed up on my arms but could hardly lift my feet off the ground; Jane somehow helped me to move forward a little way, but as my weight came onto the front of my feet my waist just bent forward and I found myself looking down at the tiled floor. Jane quickly pulled me upright again and with her knee shoved my hips forward so my weight was once again on the backs of my feet. I was now upright and breathing in as quickly as I could to make the feeling of faintness disappear. As I looked at myself in the large mirror the whiteness of my face slowly disappeared, to be replaced by natural colour.

'Ready to try again?' I heard Jane say.

'OK,' I replied.

I breathed in deeply, filling my lungs with oxygen before I pushed up once again on the parallel bars. With all my effort I lifted myself and my feet up off the floor, as I did so Jane pushed me forward then, as I lowered down, I pushed my hips forward so my weight returned to the backs of my feet.

'Well done, Andy, that was much better,' Jane said from behind me. She gave me a moment or two to relax and prepare myself for another go. We tried again and again until I had almost reached the far end of the bars and could nearly touch myself in the mirror.

'OK, Andy, I think that will do for today,' Jane said, then called out to another physiotherapist, Chris, to give her a hand to help me back into my chair.

As I sat there and watched Jane remove the bandages and plaster casts from my legs, it dawned on me that whatever I was going to do from now on was not going to be easy, whether it was washing my face or trying to walk. Jane lifted my feet up onto the foot plates of my chair. 'You can go on now if you want, Andy,' she said as she laid my plaster casts to one side. I looked across and saw one of the sets of pulleys was not being used.

'I think I will do some pulleys if it's all right with you,' I said.

Jane fixed me up in them, then had to leave to visit one of her new arrivals in bed. 'Poor sod,' I thought, 'little does he know that in a few months he will be struggling like I am now.' I carried on doing my pulleys until my arms could take no more, then returned to the ward. It seemed I was finishing my therapy later and later each evening. I sat at one of the tables, half watching the telly and half thinking about the afternoon in the parallel bars. 'What the hell am I trying to prove? I am never going to walk again, am I?' I said to myself. 'But what's the alternative: to crawl away into some hole and just let myself fade away until I finally die? I'm seventeen years of age. I've got my whole life ahead of me. OK, so I can't jump out of bed and walk to the loo but that's not to say I am never going to. You have just had a bad day. Things are going to get better. You're going to improve as each day passes and in a few months' time you will look back at all this and laugh about it.' My course of thought was interrupted with the return of Keith and Frank.

'Where have you two been?' I asked.

'We've been playing snooker in that little room just off the archery hall. Peter's given us the key so that we can have another game this evening. You can come with us if you like.'

I thought about it for a minute. 'I don't know if I could play now, not having much grip in my hands,' I replied.

'Come on, you can't be any worse than we are,' Frank said.

That night after tea Frank, Keith, Peter and I all pushed ourselves down to the small room where the snooker table was. Frank had had the insight to bring a bandage with him just in case I couldn't grip my cue. He would use it to tie the cue to my hand. This is what had to be done as I could not grip the cue and thrust it forward at the same time. None of us had played since our accidents and we found that we could no longer reach over and take the kind of shots that we used to, and were continually putting the rest on and off the table. Added to this, I needed both hands to push round the table and the cue was tied to my right hand and would start pointing forward then rise up into the air as I moved forward, which brought so much laughter from the others that they were almost in tears. I tried to laugh with them, but inside the tears were not of laughter but of pain and heartache at not being able to play the one game I enjoyed so much. After almost two hours, and without even finishing one game, we returned to the ward. Well, Peter and I did, while Keith and Frank decided to go down to the bowls club in the grounds of the hospital which had a licensed bar. I sat and watched the telly for a few moments then asked to be put to bed. Once I was in bed and able to pull the sheet over my face I began to shed the tears that had been in my eyes since late that afternoon. As they rolled off my cheeks I kept on repeating the same question, 'Why me, Lord? Why me?'

Thursday was one of those days that found me returning to my past, to the times when I was completely well and free of worry. I found myself thinking of times when I had walked great distances, such as the time when I was about ten years of age and was on a fifteen mile sponsored walk for the restoration of the church tower. It was summer time and a very warm Saturday afternoon. We had avoided roads when at all possible, passing through openings in large woods and following tracks along the edges of fields. Then for the last couple of miles we had walked along what was known locally as Stutton Shore, which was a small beach that ran parallel with the river for several miles. Once leaving there, we passed along the edge of a couple more fields, then ended up coming in behind the church to the small institute where orangeade and biscuits were waiting for us. I and three of my mates were the first back and I remember sitting down and putting my feet up on another chair in front of me and feeling them tingle now that the weight was lifted off them. I sat there until Dad arrived to pick me up and drive me the short distance home. That day will always remain with me just as the next one that I now recalled.

It was when I was in the scouts and was patrol leader, no less. We were on summer camp several miles out of Hastings. We were there for two weeks and were well into our final days when our leaders, Jeff and Trevor, suggested going on this long hike to acquire some badge or other. We set off in the early hours of that morning while it was still pitch black and needed torches to see where we were going. We walked along paths with the road on one side and the stone walls that were characteristic of that part of the country on the other. We had reached a sort of incline, looking down into Hastings, as dawn was about to break. We watched as in the distance the sun rose up from behind a large hill. It was the first time I had watched the sun rise and it climbed so quickly, as if someone from behind that hill had kicked it high up into the air like a football. We sat on the wall and watched it climb to its highest point, then we were off again. It was a good hour or so before we reached the shops and sea front of the coastal town. Once there we had breakfast at one of the small cafés along the front, then, after finishing toast and tea, we made our way across the road and onto the beach where we removed our socks and shoes and soaked our tired feet in the cool, salty water of the sea. After this we all laid back and took a well-earned rest. Our walk did not end there. Once we were refreshed we set off along the coast, stopping at places of importance, such as the ruined castle and the underground caves and then it was back onto the beach, finally finishing at the pier. By mid-afternoon we were all very tired and glad to see Jeff when he arrived with the van to take us back to camp. That time at Hastings, that day, that walk, had always been a fond memory of mine even before my accident, but now it held even more joy and sense of achievement each time I recalled it.

The weekend came round once again, my second time to return home. The long journey by road did not seem to get any shorter even though I was becoming more familiar with the towns and countryside that we passed through. The weekend took on the same pattern as the previous one. However, there was one big difference: Mum was there and although she wasn't allowed to do very much (such as lift things), just her presence made all the difference. The whole weekend seemed so much better than the previous one, although I still detested the fact that Dad had to help me with getting to bed and dressing and so on. With Dad helping me with these things, though, it began to bring us much closer together. Both Mum and Dad had been so good to me since my accident: loving and worrying about me in those early days when they wondered whether I was going to live or die; then later, giving me the encouragement to keep trying to have a go at everything that was asked of me; and now, letting me return home and helping me to return slowly to a domestic environment — not always possible for everyone who has had this kind of accident. Some of the patients' families just found they couldn't cope with their sons and daughters now that they were paralysed and in wheelchairs. Others, however, didn't have a chance to try, as their son might have been too severely injured, and would need the constant medical care that could only come within the hospital.

The different members of my family arrived and left as the weekend drew on and there were also my close friends and Kate, of course. It was soon Sunday afternoon and time to leave. The time had all too quickly slipped by and I was once again in the process of saying my goodbyes. Although I was becoming much harder at times like this, there would still be the inevitable lump in my throat when it was time to say goodbye to my mum, dad, Kate and the family. But once we had pulled away and had travelled some distance the feeling would slowly fade away. On this return journey to the hospital it was to be just Dad, my brother-in-law, John, and me. John had come along to do the return journey later that night so giving Dad a break from the driving, as Terry had done the previous time.

When we got to the hospital and Dad pushed me down the ward I noticed how much quieter it was than usual — even the lads who still had visitors with them were talking almost in a whisper. John and Dad had a cup of tea with me, then started to make a move for home. I watched from the window as they drove past the ward and then out of the gates. Now that they were gone I asked if I could be put to bed as the long journey always tired me out.

The following morning the atmosphere was a little bit brighter, but I could still feel there was something up.

'Hey, Lawrence, what's up with everybody?' I asked as he came over to my bed. 'Anyone would think they'd lost a fiver and found a penny.'

'Haven't you heard?'

'Heard what?' I asked.

'It's Ernie. He died while you were away at the weekend.'

'Died? How the hell did that happen?'

'Well, he was just lying there and then he called to Max and asked him if he would read a piece from the Bible to him. Then a little while later he was gone. Max knew there was something up and called out to the nurse and orderlies but all their efforts were to no avail.'

'I sensed there was something up when I got back last night, but it never struck me that poor old Ernie might have died. No wonder everyone was a bit quiet. How strange he should ask Max to read him a bit out of the Bible like that, just before he went. He must have known,' I said to myself.

For several days after Ernie's death there was a very noticeable atmosphere, which was understandable, of course, because it was the first time one of us patients had passed on. But after some time had passed we knew we were still living and had to get on with our lives as usual. In one way I felt sorry for Ernie's family, his wife and children, but also I couldn't help thinking it was a nice way out. Since his accident he had suffered from hallucinations and with breathing difficulties. Now, let's face it, he wouldn't have to struggle on trying to achieve the smallest things in life. He was in his sixties, I was only seventeen and I was finding it hard enough — just think what it would have been like for him. No, if I speak the truth, he was best out of it.

Chapter 15
You Will Never Walk Again

For the rest of us left in the ward, things were progressing for all of us. Keith was now up on his callipers — these were like leg irons that fitted under the trousers and with them and crutches he could walk in a kind of fashion. Mind you, it wasn't easy. I would watch him as he moved his crutches forward and then swung his hips and legs afterwards. The amount of strength it took to walk this way could be seen if you looked at his hands: they would turn white as he gripped his crutches and forced himself forward. He would only have to walk several feet this way and the perspiration would drip from his forehead and large patches of dampness would form around his armpits.

For Frank, however, it was much easier. He had now gained almost all the use in his left leg except for a dropped foot for which he needed just a small calliper that fitted into the shoe to hold it up. Having the ability to bend his leg he could move it forward, straighten it, then bring the other one up to it. The right leg was held straight by a full calliper so that it was just a matter of transferring his weight onto it, bending the left leg again, moving it forward, then pulling the right foot up to it and so on. In my own small way I was improving in the parallel bars with my plaster cast and generally in everything I did — such as my archery and swimming. The bow that I used in archery had been changed for a much stronger one, and with this my aim improved dramatically, to the point where I was regularly getting four or five golds out of every round that I fired. My swimming too had improved above all recognition and I no longer had the fear of drowning that I think we all feel when we first enter the pool after an accident like mine.

Although some of us were improving, not all of us were so fortunate. The two Peters, for instance, were at a kind of crossroads of life but for completely different reasons. The first Peter (who had been knocked down by that lorry in Germany, was slowly giving up. He would make excuses not to get out of bed and would eat next to nothing at meal times, which resulted in him getting very thin; and as he became thinner his protruding bones would rub against sheets resulting in pressure sores: they in turn kept him in bed. When he finally decided he wanted to get out of bed again, with these problems and the mental strain that he was under (which I may add we all were) there came the inevitable emotional strain. His wife had rented a bungalow just a couple of miles away from the hospital and even took a part-time job in the hospital helping out in the other wards. But for some reason, in Peter's eyes, she could do no right: he was continually upsetting her and it amazed us all the way she took all this aggro and still remained with him.

The second Peter had other things which somehow helped him cope with life. His mother and father were devout Catholics and they, plus the regular visits by the priests, seemed to be convincing him that it was the will of God that this should have happened to him. I remember one day this priest sat down and began to talk to Frank, Keith and me about how our accidents were a way of God saying, 'Look, you're going the wrong way in life and now I am pointing you in the right way again.' This I could not believe. The God and Jesus I knew were loving people and no way would deliberately make someone suffer for no reason. My accident was not an act of God but a stupid mistake on my part. I wasn't looking where I was going and so hit the lorry. My belief is that he has no control over any problems that we may come across, such as disasters like earthquakes or famine. In my view he doesn't pick certain people out to contract an incurable disease such as multiple sclerosis or cancer. However, if for some reason we are confronted with a problem such as this, he gives us the strength to cope with it, and in my view helps me to get through each and every day. But getting back to Peter number two, having his parents telling him that it was God's will he should be this way stopped him from really trying that bit harder day by day. Added to his, he had to have a small operation on his bladder to help him pass his water more easily and having to have this done put him back considerably.

It was now late October and summer had finally waved goodbye, the warm sunny days being replaced by wet and cold ones. Stoke Mandeville began to show its age. One morning as I pushed myself up to occupational therapy, I had to manoeuvre round buckets positioned to catch the drips from the leaking roof in the corridors and I watched as several orderlies mopped up large puddles that had formed overnight. That day a film crew arrived to make a small programme about how bad the hospital was becoming. The huts the wards were in had been there since the middle of the Second World War when they had been used for the very severely burnt, but now it was nearly forty years later and the many winters that they had seen had taken their toll. The programme went out later that week, but like all things, it was seen and then forgotten about — except by us who were living there.

As I was now very busy during the day with dressing or typing in the mornings and physiotherapy in the afternoons I tried to find things to do to pass the time between having our evening meal and the time when I went to bed. Keith found out about films being shown every Wednesday in

Ward Four and in the coming weeks we watched several good ones, such as 'The Shootist' with John Wayne and 'The Iron Cross' with James Coburn. On other nights I'd pop across to Ward Two for a game of Backgammon for five pence a point with a bloke called Bob, who had had to return to hospital because of pressure sores. And on the odd occasion I even went down to the bowls club with Keith and Frank for a drop of the hard stuff. But there were still times when I found myself sitting alone in the dimly lit corridor just outside the ward late into the evening. There I could sit, turning over all that had happened to me in the last six months without the feeling of being watched. 'Why was I better than Peter and not as good as Frank? Is there a reason for all this madness that I have gone through? What direction is my life going to take now?' And so on. There I would sit, contemplating all these things until I was either interrupted by the orderlies coming to do their night shift or maybe by a visitor who thought he needed to stop and talk to me before finally leaving the hospital. Although I was here with others the same as myself, some better, some worse, in my mind I was alone. The pressure would become so strong that the only way for me to release it would be to go to bed and pull the covers over my face and cry until there were no tears left. Now when things built up or went wrong I found there were no tears left. I had cried all that I was going to cry and as for God, well, he didn't care because if he did he would have helped me get well which he hadn't done. I was becoming hard mentally and no matter what was dished out to me I took it and registered no feeling one way or another. Even though I was going through this stage in my life, I couldn't give up the belief that one day I was going to get completely well again, and with this in mind I continued to put all my effort and aggression into my therapy.

October was drawing to a close and by this time I had been home several weekends. Most times Dad would pick me up and then bring me back on Sunday, but when he couldn't make it others (such as my brother, Bruce, or brothers-in-law, John and Dave) would help out by doing one of the journeys. If they couldn't do it, there was always Terry who would willingly offer his services.

One Monday I had just returned from one of my weekends home, I was sitting in line ready for my turn in the Doctors' Office. The door opened, Keith reversed out and in I went.

'Hello, Andrew,' Dr Silver said as the door was closed behind me.

'Hello,' I replied.

As he flicked through my notes he asked the different heads of departments how I was getting on. First came the Head of Physio. 'He has done very well all round: he needs little or no help with his transfers from bed to chair and back again; his arms are much stronger now through his efforts at the pulleys and archery; he is also up in the parallel bars on plaster casts,' she finished off.

'Next please,' I said to myself and it was the Head of Occupational Therapy's turn.

'His dressing has improved; he only needs a little help with his trousers, shoes and socks; he washes his own hair, brushes his teeth and feeds himself very well. He can also set out and type a letter reasonably well as long as he uses an electronic typewriter.'

'Crumbs, they are bumming me up today,' I thought to myself. Now it was Sister Shilton's turn.

'How many weekends has he been home now?' Dr Silver asked her.

'Four so far and I got in contact with the Social Services and they say now that his parents have moved into their bungalow everything is acceptable for his return home.'

Now it was my turn and as Dr Silver began to speak to me all the other members present in that office looked up from their papers and fixed their eyes on me.

'Well, Andrew, you have done very well. I think we can now set a date for when you can return home permanently.

Let's say the 22nd of next month,' he added as he turned to get acknowledgment from the others present. 'What do you say to that?'

'I don't know really. Can't I stop a bit longer so that I can carry on with my standing up in the parallel bars?' I had been wondering why he had been asking all these questions about me, but going home — I wasn't really ready. 'I was going to improve and only leave here when I could walk out of the front door,' I said to myself.

'You can carry on in the parallel bars up until you leave, but I must tell you YOU WILL NEVER WALK AGAIN,' he replied.

I looked across at him. I had heard the words but couldn't take them in. I am not saying that from time to time over the last six months I hadn't thought that I wasn't going to walk again, but I had always pushed that thought from my mind and replaced it with belief and hope. But to hear Dr Silver telling me that I wasn't going to walk, well that was a different matter. My heart filled with sadness and I blinked my eyes several times so as not to cry in front of those others. Then I filled with anger, and I lifted my head up and looked straight at him and within myself said, 'That's what you bloody think. I will walk again if it's the last thing I do. Then I will return here and boot you right in the shin just to prove my point.'

I had lowered my head so many times over the last months when I had been embarrassed or at the times when I was at the depths of despair, but this time I held my head high and it was Dr Silver's turn to lower and turn his head.

'OK, Andrew, I think that's all,' he said. Then the door was opened and I pushed myself down to the ward, still thinking about what I had just been told.

'You all right, Andy?' Keith asked as I pushed past him to get to the French windows at the bottom of the ward.

'Yer, I'm fine, thanks,' I replied.

As I sat near the window I watched the rain trickle down the panes and tried to find a reason why Dr Silver should say such a thing, giving me no incentive or hope to carry on and then tell me I could go home — in other words, this is as far as you're going to get. 'All I can say is, Dr Silver, you're one hell of a bastard and that's no mistake.' I felt someone touch me on the shoulder and, as I turned, I saw Jane standing by my side.

'You OK, Andy?' she asked caringly.

'Silver says I can go home next month and as an added bonus he politely told me I was never going to walk again,' I replied.

'Well, you have got to leave here sometime and look on the bright side — at least you have got another month . . . and as for what he said about you not walking, you don't believe everything people tell you, do you? Anyway, he tells everyone the same thing. Imagine if he said, "OK, Andy, by the end of the year you will be walking again," and you weren't, how you would feel then? You would probably sue the hospital for false promises. This way he safeguards himself and the hospital and leaves it up to you to prove him wrong.'

What she said made a lot of sense and just talking to her had made me feel a whole lot better than I had done a few minutes earlier.

She went on, 'I cannot say if you will walk again, but what's the alternative? To give up trying altogether and remain the way you are, is that what you want?'

She was right, of course: there was no alternative. I had to keep going for myself. It was I who would have to spend every day in a wheelchair and have to go without all the things I had once taken for granted if I did not achieve my aim in life. And with this in mind I set out to prove Dr Silver wrong.

My final month at Stoke Mandeville began and, with its start, I had to say goodbye to Keith. As I watched him get his things together the memories of the last few months returned to my mind. At first he had not wanted to have anything to do with any of us; then, once he had got in his chair and was working towards his goal in life he changed. I remember him bringing me a bowl of soup while I was still in bed in those early weeks and fixing me up with my spoon in the strap that I used. It was he who had got me into the bad habit of backing the horses. It was he who pushed me on to do more and more pulleys each day, and again it was he who had helped me feel as good as him and Frank by getting me to play cards and snooker. He also got me to go along to watch the films in Ward Four on Wednesdays and even go down to the bowls club for a drink where the majority of people were walking about and not in wheelchairs. Together we had talked a lot over the months and knew when the other was cheesed off or really on a high. Both Keith and Frank had been the jokers in the ward, the ones that had kept everyone going when at times they might have given up.

'You off, then, mate?' I said as I got near his bed.

'Yer, Dad's putting the things in the motor.'

'Best of luck, Keith. I've got your address and phone number so I'll give you a ring from time to time to see how you're getting on.'

'Yer, OK, Andy, and if you haven't rung, after you get home I'll ring you.'

'OK, see you.'

'Yer, bye,' and with that I pushed myself off to the physio.

That night, without the presence of Keith the ward was much quieter and it was strange not to see him and Frank charging about, deliberately smashing into one another in their wheelchairs. Frank and I watched the television and played a few hands of cards.

'It's going to be quiet without old Keith,' I said.

'Yer, I'll miss him,' Frank replied.

The evening drew on until it was time to turn in. I lay there listening to the other lads at the far end of the ward still calling to one another, just like we all had done when we were going through that long period of being in bed all day. There was only the light from the full moon outside and I thought about the prospect of going home for good in a couple of weeks' time. 'How will I cope? It's bad enough at weekends. I'm frightened to death that something's going to go wrong, such as falling out of my chair or getting a water infection. It's not that I want to stay here forever, either. Of course there are things I miss like being with Kate and my family and having Mum's cooking, but what will happen? What will I do for therapy?' These things continued to turn over in my mind until I finally dropped off to sleep.

In the middle of the afternoon on the following day I was enjoying my archery when Pete came up to see me. 'Andy, there are a couple of blokes making a recording for Radio Two about how sport benefits people in wheelchairs and they wondered if you would have a chat with them,' he said.

'Yer, OK.'

Peter removed the bandages that had been holding the bow to my hand, and all the others that I used to stop myself from falling out of my chair while firing my arrows. I moved over to the corner of the hall and then the chap switched on his tape recorder.

'Why do you do archery and do you think it benefits you in any way?' he asked.

'Well, once I had been out of bed and had built my arms up to the point where I was able to push myself around, my physiotherapist, Jane, brought me along to have a go and I found it was a sport that I could still compete in against people the same as myself and also against fit, healthy people as well. Does it benefit me, you asked? Yes, I think it does in several ways: in one way, it's helping me build my shoulders and arms up in an enjoyable way; in another, it's making me compete again in life.'

'What about when you leave here? Will you carry on doing archery?'

'I'd like to, but I'm not sure how much the equipment costs, so I will have to look into that when I get home.'

'OK, thank you very much for talking to us and all the best for the future.'

'Thanks,' I replied and then set off back to the ward feeling quite chuffed at the thought of being on the radio. I recall it going out a week or so later but unfortunately I had forgotten all about it. Luckily, Mum, Dad and a few friends remembered and listened in with interest to what I had to say.

With Keith's departure came other moves in the ward. Salim had to go into a side ward. He came from a place called Abu Dhabi, a port in one of the Arab Emirates. I believe he had worked for a prince or someone quite high up as a driver and they, or the country, were paying for him to be at Stoke Mandeville. All in all there were about a dozen men from the Middle East, including a prince who had a private room in Ward One. Frank was given a room in the hostel as he was now capable of looking after himself. Although he slept over there, he still returned to the ward for his meals. Now things had been changed around there was space for a couple of new patients. As I watched one of the new lads being settled in, it dawned on me that hospitals are no more than conveyor belts: we all enter severely ill and the doctors and nurses take care of us and help us improve until they think we are ready to leave; then, no sooner have we emptied our lockers and vacated our beds than someone else arrives to take our place. 'And this is how it will remain,' I thought. 'Well, that is for as long as there are sick people who need the care that only hospitals can provide.'

As time was slipping by I threw all my effort into my different therapies, trying to improve on everything before I left. As I pushed myself to and fro from the different departments I noticed others who had not been out of bed very long, who had collars round their necks and who were about to start the long, hard fight on the road to recovery. Then I saw others who had been here as long as I had: some unable to move anything, others walking around with just a stick. As I looked at those who were dependent on someone for everything, I thought how lucky I was. Then, as I looked at those walking there was a tinge of jealousy — not spiteful in any way but just the fact that they were the lucky ones, and how I wished that I too could have been.

The days had now run into weeks and Dad would be arriving the next day to take me home for good. That night I sat in the ward, wondering if there was anything that I could have done over the last seven months which might have improved me even more. 'Could I have worked harder at the different tasks Jane had set me? Was there anything Dr Silver could have done in those early weeks which would have given me back the use in my muscles and limbs? And what about these last couple of weeks after I heard that I was going home? Was there something new I could have tried so that I could walk out of the hospital tomorrow rather than being pushed?' It was all turning over and over in my mind, but there was one continual thought that kept returning: 'You must not give up; you have got to keep trying.' It was that stubborn streak in me that I had always had; whenever someone had said I couldn't do something, I would do it. There had been many times in my short life when someone had said that I couldn't do this or that.

For instance, there was the time when a group of us were sitting outside the local shops one summer's afternoon and one of my mates said, 'I bet you can't hit that piece of wood between the two frames of glass on that bloke's front door with that stone you're messing about with.' No sooner had he said the words than I was up on my feet, had taken aim and fired at the door in question. Unfortunately, he was right: I missed the wood and hit the lower pane of glass sending a large resounding crack throughout the immediate vicinity. There were other times, too, when people had dared me to do things such as jumping off scaffolding into a pile of sand by the new houses that were being built on the near-by estate, or scrumping apples from the orchards that we passed on the way home from school.

I suppose there is one escapade that towers above them all, though. It was when I was sixteen — I know that because I had my moped and was working at the garage. It was summer-time yet again and Kate and I were in her bedroom listening to records as usual. Kate would always get ready for bed before I left and the sight of her in her pink nightie always had the same effect on me. It was getting pretty late by now and I knew I had to get up for work the following morning, and that if I stayed much longer I would want to stop all night which I knew wasn't possible.

'I have got to go, Kate,' I said as I climbed off her bed.

'Why don't you sneak back and climb up onto the oil tank and into here when Mum's gone to bed? Dad won't be back till tomorrow,' she suggested.

'You're joking,' I replied. 'Even if I came back you would be asleep and wouldn't even wake up.'

'You're scared,' was her answer.

'All right then, I will come back but you had better be awake.'

With that I kissed her goodnight and slid downstairs. Just before I went out of the door I put my head round the sitting room door and said goodnight to her mum and sister Gillian. As I put my moped in the garden at home the thought of going back to Kate's and spending the night with her became more and more tempting. I went indoors and made out that I had locked the door. Everyone else was in bed, so this made things much easier. I pretended that I had gone to bed then, after about half an hour, I crept out of my room holding my boots in my arms and, as quickly as possible, crept downstairs. All the time, though, my heart was in my mouth and I was wondering if someone had heard the stairs creak and was coming to investigate. I slipped my boots and coat on as quietly as possible, then left the house. Not daring to start my bike outside the back of the house, I pushed it out of the estate before finally turning the ignition. So there I was on my way to Kate's, when suddenly my bike started to splutter then died on me. 'Oh shit. I've run out of petrol.' I had known I was low but thought I would easily get there and back. What could I do now? I had come this far but still had a good mile to go — well, in for a penny, in for a pound. I pushed my bike behind the hedge of a nearby field and then set off on foot.

It must have been midnight by the time I reached Kate's drive, but as I looked up there were still lights in the kitchen and her dad's car was in the drive. 'Oh damn. He's come back tonight.' I was crouching beside the neighbour's car when suddenly their back door opened and out came Mr Chorley — Kate's dad — and their dog, Kas. I hid behind his car, my heart pounding like a copper drum. At this point I was something glad I had got a strong ticker otherwise I think I would have taken my final breath right there and then. Mr Chorley opened his car door to reach for his case, then called to Kas. By this time Kas had got scent of me and duly found me kneeling behind the neighbour's car. 'Go on, Kas.' I mouthed the words without making a sound. 'Come on, Kas,' Mr Chorley called again, and by this time he was only a matter of feet away from me. I covered my face at the same time searching in my mind for an answer to explain what I was doing there at that time of night and why I was behind this car. The only feeble excuse I could come up with was that I had lost some money I needed for the morning and thought it could be behind the car. It wasn't very good, I knew, but it was the best I could do. To my amazement Mr Chorley failed to see me and both Kas and he returned indoors. I let out a huge sigh of relief and sat back, not believing my luck. As I sat there the light went out in the kitchen and then the bathroom light was put on in its place. In the quietness of that time of night I could hear as Mr Chorley ran a bath and now I knew for sure that the chances of getting to Kate's bedroom were nil. Feeling thoroughly dejected I set off back home. I finally reached my bike but by the time I had pushed it the remaining half mile I was completely shattered. Holding my breath, I crept back indoors and up to bed. It was now well past one in the morning but as I lay there I couldn't help thinking how lucky I had been an hour ago. My eyes closed and I fell into a deep sleep.

As I recalled this memory, I knew that was the type of determination I had got to show now, just because Dr Silver said I wouldn't walk again. I have to go home and prove him wrong. 'I am going home tomorrow and there must be someone or something out there that will help me to regain the use in my limbs. That's what I have to take with me from here and hold it close to my heart and believe it for however long it takes to come true.'

Yesterday had now become today and time to clear out my locker and say goodbye to all those who had helped me over the last seven months. I had already said my farewells to my friends in the Occupational Therapy department the day before, and last night had pushed myself up to Ward Four to say goodbye to Peter who had just got over his operation.

Dad had arrived and was packing the things from my locker. As I watched him take out the bundles of letters and cards, I remembered how grateful I had been to receive them during the many weeks in bed and how they had kept me in touch with life back home. He was just finishing putting the rest of my things in my case when Sister Shilton called to him to give him all the medical equipment I would need until I had sorted something out with my local doctor.

'I will be putting your case and these other things in the car while you say goodbye to everyone,' Dad said.

As I pushed myself up the ward, I stopped and said goodbye to all those who were in bed.

'Bye, Andy. Good luck, mate, for the future,' they said as I pushed past their beds.

Then I smiled and said farewell to all the staff who were on duty and Dr Silver. By this time I had got a big lump coming to my throat, but there was still one very special person that I had got to say goodbye to. I had asked Mum if she could buy me some chocolates for the staff on the ward and had given them to Sister Shilton as I left, but I had also asked Mum to get me a porcelain rose and vase to give to Jane, somehow to repay her for everything that she had done for me. Dad pushed me down to the physio department. I knocked on the staff door and Jane came out.

'Just come to say goodbye and give you this small present as a sort of thank you for all that you have done for me over the last months.'

I watched as she undid the wrapping paper.

'Oh, it's lovely, Andy, but there was no need to buy me anything,' she said.

'Well, it was just my way of saying thank you.'

'It's me who should be saying thank you and I do,' and with that she bent down and kissed me on the cheek. 'I have also got a present for you. Hang on there a minute,' and off she went into the department, only to return seconds later with two sets of plaster casts and several crepe bandages. 'You can take these home with you as I believe your dad is having a set of parallel bars made up for you at his works.' She laid them on my lap and as our eyes met she could tell I was apprehensive about leaving. 'Don't worry, Andy, everything is going to be fine and you're coming back in six weeks for a check up so I will look forward to seeing you then.'

'OK, Jane. See you in six weeks!' With that Dad turned my chair and pushed me up and out of the corridor to the car.

It was strange. Here I was, on my way home — something I had been longing for ever since the first day I had arrived at Stoke Mandeville. But now that it had finally come, part of me did not want to go. Dad tried to chat to me but I gazed out of the window as the tears rolled down my cheeks.

'Come on , Andy, everything's going to be all right,' he said. 'Don't worry, mate. We will find someone who will be able to help you.'

I pulled myself together. Dad was right: there must be someone who could help me and if there was I would find him.

Three hours later on this cold, wet November afternoon we were going through East Bergholt.

'Do you want to stop at Kate's before going home?' Dad asked.

'Yer, OK,' I replied.

We drew up outside her house and as Dad switched his engine off out came Kate and her mum and dad. I wound the window down.

'Hello, babe,' she said and leant in and kissed me. 'I will come down later after tea.'

'Yer, great,' and for the first time I was pleased to be home.

'Do you want to come in?' Mrs Chorley asked.

'No, we'd better not as I think Joan is probably wondering where we have got to,' Dad replied.

'See you later then, Katie.'

'OK. Bye.'

Dad reversed out of their drive and back onto the main road. Then a few minutes later there I was pulling up outside my own home and, as I looked into the lounge, Mum, Jo and Lou were up out of their seats and at the window.

Dad helped me out of the car and pushed me down the path and into the bungalow.

'Hello dear, welcome home,' Mum said as she filled the kettle to make a pot of tea. It was as if I had never been away. Jo and Lou helped Dad bring the rest of my things in and took them straight down to my bedroom.

'Come and see your room,' Lou said with excitement. I slowly pushed myself down the long hall that ran the length of the bungalow and awkwardly manoeuvred the different bends until I finally reached my room. Dad had redecorated it for me with brown and cream walls and a new white wardrobe and as he laid the rest of my stuff on the floor I thanked him for it. 'It's really nice, Dad.' I sat and looked out of my window. 'Can you plug my cassette recorder in for me, please, Jo?' I asked.

She plugged it in for me then they went back into the lounge, leaving me alone for a few minutes. I placed one of my favourite tapes in my recorder and as the first few words of the song filled my ears — 'Gee, it's great to be back home, home is where I want to be' — I reminded myself how lucky I really was to be home and how I could have been dead or so severely injured that I would never have come home.

Chapter 16
The End of Something Good

The next few days were a testing time for both me and my family as I tried to settle in back home again. I was still having to rely on others to help me, and Dad more than most. He was getting up during the night to turn me and also helping me wash and dress in the mornings. By the time I was dressed and had my breakfast it would be late into the morning; the rest of the day was taken up by reading the paper or sitting watching the telly until either my sisters returned home from school or work or some friends called to see me. By this time it would be tea time, then after that Kate would more often than not arrive to spend the evening with me. And this was how I spent my days in those first couple of weeks. By now it was only a matter of a week or so before Christmas. 'How will I cope with being in this wheelchair at this time of year?' I wondered to myself.

As Christmas was approaching everyone around me seemed to be busy getting things ready for the festivities. Dad put up all the trimmings, Jo and Lou decorated the tree and Mum was slaving over the oven baking cakes and boiling puddings.

My sisters and brothers-in-law were calling in and casually dropping hints as to what both they and the children would like for Christmas. Although I smiled and tried to join in all that was happening so as not to upset Mum and Dad, it was as if I was on the outside looking in at all these things that were going on around me. Somehow I couldn't get involved. Then came the obvious question from the different members of the family: 'What would you like, Andy, for Christmas?' To which my answer was always, 'Oh, I don't mind, anything would be nice.' But every time I said these words there was the same thought in my mind: if only I could have the use back in my muscles and limbs, there was nothing more that I could ask for or want; and if I could have this, I would give all my other presents away to charity and to those who were less fortunate than me. Would my wish be granted? All I could do was sit and wait.

By Christmas Eve, Mum had done all my shopping for me and Jo had helped me wrap up the majority of my presents and, as it was the time of year for visiting, I had several mates call with cans of beer. First was a couple of my local friends, Ernie and my old mate, Terry. They had called in on their way home from work. Terry you know of from earlier in my book but Ernie, well, we had been mates several years, since the time I moved from Palfrey up to Broomknoll. We had often worked together at weekends while we were both still at school. I remember when I was saving up enough money to put down a deposit on my moped I would do my paper round from Monday to Friday; then on Saturday mornings both Ernie and I would work at Tom Goodchild's, the local farmer, from seven till half twelve; then I would change and bike four miles to the Little Chef restaurant on the busy dual carriageway from Ipswich to London. There I would work from three till nine as a washer-upper-cum-waiter. On Sundays both Ernie and I would clean a couple of cars in the morning. In the afternoon I would again cycle to the Little Chef for another stint of washing up etc. But it was during the times at the farm or cleaning those cars that I came to appreciate what a hard working bloke Ernie really was, and at times when his other mates hadn't got time for him I like to think I had.

Both Terry and Ernie stopped with me for most of the afternoon drinking beer and talking of old times. After they left in came a couple of mates from the garage I had worked at before my accident. There was Les, the bloke who I had been training with, and Andy, the other apprentice, who had started at the same time as me and who had broken both his arms several months earlier. They brought in yet more cans of beer and as we sat drinking and talking Les produced this cheque from his inside pocket.

'Here you are, Andy. It's a cheque for all the money we raised while you were in hospital. It's from everyone in the garage.' As he passed it to me I said, 'Crumbs, I don't know what to say. Are you sure it's for me?'

'Yer, go on, Andy, take it — it's from all of us,' Andy chipped in.

'OK, thanks ever so much. It's really kind of you all; all I can say is thanks again.'

After that was over they stayed a bit longer, drinking and telling me all that was happening in the garage.

'You will have to come and see us all in the New Year,' Andy said.

'I don't know,' I replied. 'I would rather wait until I can walk in, then I will.'

They stayed a bit longer, chatting away, then got up to go. As they were going out of the door I thanked them again for the money and then they were gone. As I looked at the cheque they had given me it brought a lump to my throat to think of all the people who had contributed to it and through their generosity the word kindness was truly being lived.

Christmas Day. The morning we all look forward to all year, and time to open our presents. My brother and his wife, Jackie, had arrived the night before to spend Christmas with us. As we sat round, each with our piles of parcels beside us, Lou was opening every one as if there was a stopwatch on her and Dad was so slow you could make a pot of tea in the time it took him to remove the paper from just one present. Then came me and as I struggled to undo the tape Bruce finally came to my rescue by offering to start each parcel for me. Fortunately (or unfortunately, whichever you may feel) almost all my family had decided to play it safe by buying me a jumper. 'Well, at least I won't get cold,' I thought to myself.

The festivities passed by without any problems really and that night I even ventured up to Kate's for the first time. I had always got on well with Kate's parents and sisters, Sue and Gillian. They had all visited me frequently during my stay in hospital and now here I was back in their home and they were making me very welcome as they had always done. Kate helped me undo my presents from her mum and dad.

'Oh, thank you,' I said as I held up yet another jumper. Then Kate handed me her present and I said to myself, 'Oh, please let it be anything but a jumper,' and to my joy it was a leather bomber jacket. 'Oh thanks, babe. It's really great,' I said. Dad had brought in my presents for them before he left and I asked Kate to hand them round.

'Can I open mine now?' Kate asked, and as I watched her tear off the paper a picture on the front of the box became visible. 'Oh, Andy, it's lovely,' she turned and said.

'What is it, Kate?' asked her mum.

'It's a portable telly.' She came over and kissed me. 'Thanks, babe,' she said.

'Well, I knew you would like one and if I hadn't bought you one you would have wanted mine in a few months' time.'

Her sister's bedroom was downstairs and knowing that I wouldn't be able to climb stairs for a little while Kate had moved into the downstairs bedroom so that whenever I came to her house we could go in there for some privacy. Now that she would have a telly in there we could watch that in the evenings. I stayed until Dad came back for me later that evening. All in all it hadn't been a bad Christmas.

The following day Kate came down to me for the day and then, as always, after all the preparation and build-up it was all too quickly over until the following year.

New Year's Eve, and as I sat with a glass of wine in my hand waiting for the clock to strike midnight I said to myself, 'Oh, please Lord, let there be someone come into my life who will be able to help me get the use back into my limbs again.' I asked with all my heart, 'Please let this come true.' Then both Mum, Dad and I clinked our glasses together and drank the New Year in.

The first couple of weeks of January passed by with me just sitting about all day as usual, but I was beginning to find that by not doing any exercise I was becoming very stiff. So I asked Dad if he would buy me a piece of foam mattress so that I could start doing some of my therapy on my own at home. Now, once I was up and dressed and had had my breakfast, Dad or Mum would help me out of my wheelchair down onto this mattress that was laid on the floor, either in the lounge or in my bedroom. I would roll about there trying to loosen myself up for maybe an hour or so, then Mum or Dad would again help me back into my chair. Although it wasn't very much it was a start and I was still trying. I suppose I had been doing these exercises several weeks when Dad came home from work one particular day and told me about this chap in Ipswich he had heard about. 'He is an osteopath and physical medicine specialist apparently, and several people swear by him. One lady goes to him regularly whenever she puts her back out and suggested that I took you. What do you say?'

'Why not? I have nothing to lose,' I replied.

Dad got on the phone and booked me an apointment later that week. As I listened I heard Dad explaining to this Mr Parker exactly what was wrong with me. When he got off the phone I asked what the osteopath had said.

'After I told him about your accident and about you being in Stoke Mandeville he told me to bring you along on Thursday afternoon and he would see what he could do.'

The next couple of days slipped quickly by as I eagerly awaited my visit to Mr Parker and I couldn't help thinking that maybe he was the one who was to help me walk again.

The big day arrived and as we pulled up outside his house I couldn't help noticing a small plaque on the wall near his front door, just like the ones doctors and dentists have. Dad got out of the car, went up the couple of steps and rang the door. It was opened by a man wearing a white coat rather like the ones dentists use. I chuckled to myself as I thought 'I've come about my neck, not my teeth.'

Anyway both Dad and the person I found out a few minutes later was Mr Parker came down to the car. Mr Parker opened the door, then bent down.

'Hello, Andy. I am Mr Parker. I think the easiest way to get you in is for me to carry you. OK?' He slipped his arms underneath me, then lifted me out of the car, carried me indoors and into what I assumed was his lounge. There he laid me down on one of those doctor's couches. He then sat down beside me and asked how my accident had happened, how long I had been in hospital and when I had come home. Then, he got up and examined me to see what movement I had and also if I could feel what toe he was touching. Once satisfied he moved up to my head. 'I'm just going to have a feel round your neck. There is nothing to worry about.'

At this point I must explain that I hated anybody touching my neck as I thought having broken it once I could quite easily do it again if I wasn't careful. He gently massaged my neck, then every so often pushed his fingers deep into it to feel each vertebra. 'OK, Andy, thank you. Now I will take you back to the car.' He picked me up once again and carried me out, placing me back in the front seat. 'I am just going to have a chat with your dad. Won't be long.' He closed the door of the car, then went back indoors.

'I suppose he's telling Dad there is nothing he can do for me,' I thought as I gazed out of the car window and down the road. Then the door opened and I could see Dad smiling as he shook Mr Parker's hand and said, goodbye. As Dad got into the car, then started up and pulled away I said, 'Oh, please Lord, let it be good news.' For a minute or two I did not dare ask what he had said, but as we turned into the main road I could not hold myself any longer. 'What did he say, Dad? Can he do anything for me?' I asked, almost not wanting to hear the answer in case it wasn't good news.

'Well, he said that when he examined your neck if he had found a lump round near the vertebrae you damaged then there would have been nothing he could have done for you as it would have meant that your spinal cord was severed completely and your nerves were just one big mess. But he said there seems to be nothing wrong with yours. He could feel no lump and he reckons that he will have you walking again in two years.'

The words were like sweet music to my ears. Oh, I could not believe it: at last I had found someone who believed I could walk again. I wondered if it was a dream that I was living and if what I had just heard Dad say was true; but it only took one look at his face to tell me it was true. If someone had given him a million pounds it would not have made him as happy as he was at that moment. He returned home and told Mum and the rest of the family the good news, and after all the tears had been wiped away it was as if a huge cloud had been lifted from all of us and they all, as well as myself, could now look forward to the future with joy rather than sadness.

Going to Mr Parker's became a weekly routine. When I went back the second week he carried me into his dining room where a large mattress was laid on top of the table for me to lie on. He explained that his clients usually went into a room down some steps in his house but as it would be even more difficult to take me there this was the next best thing. As we talked I found out more about his earlier life. Apparently he had been in the RAF and was a PT instructor and also was in their gymnastic team. While doing some display he was involved in a terrible accident himself: for some reason one of the landing mats had been put in the wrong place, the first man had been unable to roll away and several of the team landed on top of one another; Mr Parker had broken his back and had been paralysed himself for many weeks. Through his own experience he could appreciate exactly what I was going through. Before I left he turned me over onto my stomach and got me to do a few press-ups and then, slapping the backs of my legs, made me concentrate on trying to bend my legs up so that the heels of my feet touched my buttocks. Then, turning me over, he tried to get me to do some sit-ups by pulling up on my arms. To finish off with, I again had to concentrate on my legs and feet and will them to move for me again.

'This is what I want you to do every day from now on. Spend an hour or so on it, OK, Andy?' he said as he lifted me off his dining room table and carried me back to the car.

'OK, Mr. Parker. I will have a go,' I replied. When he put me into the car, I had only been in there for half an hour but by the time I left I was completely shattered.

As each week passed I was improving on everything I did. As far as press-ups and sit-ups were concerned, I did more and more every day, but all the willing in the world somehow could not make my limbs respond to what I asked of them. I did not give up and every day after breakfast until lunch time, there I was on my mattress, religiously doing my exercises. Also, by now I had had a standing frame delivered (courtesy of Stoke Mandeville) which enabled me to stand up every afternoon as long as Mum or Dad helped me up into it and then later on out of it. So again I was working towards my goal after only a short break when I first got home and this made me feel really good, as if my life was heading somewhere. You know, there was this target I had got to reach and once I had reached that one there was another a little further on and so on, until I finally reached the real one. Then I would be able to relax and take a holiday. I knew before I could have that holiday I had got to earn it.

Although my life was taking an 'up-turn', so to speak, as far as getting back on the road to physical recovery, my social life had hit an all-time low. My old mates, who only lived just up the road, did not even come to visit me. Some, I was told, found coming to see me sitting in this wheelchair very upsetting. 'Why should they be upset?' I thought. 'It's not them who has to go through the mental anguish each and every day. Let's face it, just because I am in this chair I haven't suddenly grown two heads and gone barmy in the process. OK, so I can't run about or play silly buggers at the moment, but I can still hold a conversation and play a game of cards or have a drink, and even fart if I have had beans for tea.' I was no different. The only thing was, was the chair I was sitting in: it had wheels on where theirs had legs. But when the odd mate did come and see me I noticed they tried to avoid talking about anything that involved using one's legs as if that would upset me in some way, and the look on their faces of almost disbelief when I started chatting away about motorbike racing or football was incredible. I am not blaming my mates completely for not coming to see me that often, as when they did they would usually ask me to go out with them down the pub or the club, and I almost always said, 'Thank you, but no thank you.' For at that time I could not cope with the inevitable curiosity of people who would turn and stare at me whenever I entered a pub or crowd of people. I too cannot blame them as I undoubtedly would have been the same if the shoe had been on the other foot, so to speak.

Even though my life wasn't filled with lots of friends there were still a few close people who I knew were always there. I had now grown close to Chris and Terry and their two children, Jackie and Darren, and tried to make the effort to go up to their house one evening in the week. They would sit and talk away to me and I found it was one of the few places apart from home where I could feel comfortable and where I was treated no differently from how I always had been. Then there was Jane, my mate Kim's girlfriend — well, ex-girlfriend as they had parted a month or two before; but even though she no longer went out with Kim she asked if she could still come and see me on a Saturday every two weeks and this is what she did without fail. It amazed me that a pretty girl such as herself would want to give up every other Saturday to come and visit me, but I wasn't complaining — on the contrary, I looked forward to her coming.

My other close friends were, of course, Kate's family, who had been and still were very good to me. As for me and Kate, we were beginning to drift apart. It was now May 1978. In January I had been back to Stoke Mandeville for my check up and then later that month I started to go to Mr Parker. The weeks had passed and Kate had regularly come down to mine in the evenings. March arrived and I had my eighteenth birthday and Kate bought me a watch. As the month drew on and into April she started to go out more and more in the evenings to discos and so on. Although we were still engaged, I had no power to stop her even if I had wanted to. Instead I made no fuss but tried to imagine how I would feel if I was seventeen and still well: I would want to go out and enjoy myself rather than sit in with someone who could do very little. Then came the fact that when she was out she was also going out with other blokes. Although this cut me up inside, as long as I didn't hear about it or see it I could cope with it as I felt at least this way I had still got a part of her love, rather than none of it.

The month of May and the day after the FA Cup Final. Our local football team, Ipswich, had just won the cup. It was Sunday and the team were going to go around the town in an open-decker bus ending up at the Town Hall for a Civic Reception. Kate said she was coming round that afternoon but hadn't arrived. So there I was sitting watching the team arrive at the Town Hall and, as the TV camera spanned over the crowd, who should come into focus but Kate sitting on this bloke's shoulders. To see her zoom up in front of my very eyes with this other bloke was too much. It was as if someone had stuck his hand inside my stomach and pulled all my insides out. I could not sit and watch any more just in case I saw her again. Instead I turned my chair around and pushed myself down to my bedroom where I could sit quietly and think things out. We hadn't seen much of each other over the last couple of weeks and I should have realised we couldn't carry on the way we had been and we had got to talk things out.

That night I rang her. 'Enjoy yourself this afternoon, babe?' I said when she came to the phone.

'Yer, it was OK,' was her reply.

'Can I see you, Katie, and talk?'

'Oh please, Andy, come up tomorrow night.'

The following day as I lay on my mattress I could not keep my mind on what I was supposed to be doing. Instead I kept thinking about what Kate and I were going to say to one another that evening. I had my tea but didn't feel much like eating. Then Dad took me up to Kate's, but instead of going into the lounge we went straight to her bedroom. She sat down on her bed and, as she fiddled with a bottle of nail polish and I with my lighter, we started talking about all kinds of things, consciously avoiding what we really wanted to say to one another.

Then I took the plunge. 'Well, I suppose that's it between us then, babe,' I said.

There was a short silence.

'It doesn't have to be,' Kate said, not looking up from the bottle she was twisting around in her hand.

'No, Katie, I understand. You're young and pretty and still want to go out and enjoy yourself and I can no longer take you.'

'Don't say that, Andy. I love you. I don't want us to finish. I just don't know what came over me,' she said as the tears rolled down her cheek.

'Don't start that, babe, or you will have me at it,' I said.

Then there seemed to be a never ending silence. 'Well, I suppose I had better go,' I said at last.

'No, you can't go yet, you have only just got here. Anyway, you can't go like this.'

'Well, what else is there to say, Katie?'

'All right, but if we do finish we can still see each other, can't we?' she said.

'No. There is no point in that. Anyway, your new fella wouldn't like it, would he?' I replied.

'Oh Andy, I couldn't bear not seeing you. I love you.'

It was as if someone had opened the flood gates from behind her eyes: the tears simply poured out and down her cheeks. She got up and sat on my lap flinging her arms around me. Then, laying her wet face against mine, she said, 'I don't care what anybody else says, I still want to see you.'

By now it was all too much for me and I too found tears rolling down my face. 'OK, babe, we will still see each other.'

We both wiped away the tears and I looked straight into her eyes and smiled. 'If someone saw us now they would think we had been to a funeral.'

Those few words brought a smile to her face. 'I feel like I have, but honestly, Andy, whoever I go with I will always tell them about you and if they don't like it, well, that will be the end of them.'

We just sat there, not knowing what to say to one another now after all that. Then as we smoked our fourth or fifth cigarette Kate asked, 'Do you want the ring back?'

'No, you keep it. I've no use for it,' I replied.

'You won't give up trying now this has happened, will you?' she said.

'No, I won't give up,' I replied.

'I want you to walk more than anything in the world, Andy. Please keep trying for me, because although we have broken up now, I love you so much and one day I want you to walk me up that aisle. In a way this should make you more determined.'

As I sat there I thought about what she had just said. In a way she was right: if I win my fight I also win her but if I lose, I lose everything.

Chapter 17
Crawling!

I suppose two or three weeks had passed after that evening in Kate's bedroom and we had neither phoned nor seen each other since; when, one day, the phone rang and it was her.

'OK if I come down, Andy?'

'Yer, sure. I would love to see you.' I replied.

We sat all evening, just chatting away to one another in my bedroom. When she left, we kissed and that was it. From now on this was how it would always be. Some people couldn't understand why I should still want to see her after what had happened but there were lots of reasons: one was that I knew if it hadn't been for Katie coming to see me each and every week while I was lying in hospital for three months I wouldn't have made it. For that reason alone I would always welcome her into my life; another was every time I saw her it gave me the incentive to try that bit harder; for another, we had always got on well together and knew almost exactly what the other was thinking; we could also talk easily to each other and explain how we felt and what was troubling us. I suppose there will always be a part of me that still loves Kate, either for the person she is or for what she did for me over those difficult years.

By midsummer, with the encouragement from Mr Parker

and my own hard work I had got strong enough to be able to turn myself during the night rather than have Dad come in and help me. I had also got rid of the pillows I used to lie on, plus the bag — in its place I had to use a bottle during the night but at least for part of the time I was free from all things medical. Since my accident I no longer wore pyjamas and, as I lay there stretched out in my double bed with just a quilt covering me, I would feel as if there was nothing wrong with me. I often dreamed that in the morning I would be able to sit up and walk to the bathroom like I always had done. Unfortunately when each morning arrived my dream did not become reality, but that wasn't to say it wouldn't become so in the future.

While the weather was warm I would push myself out into the garden and let the hot sun change my complexion from a palish colour to a brighter one. As I sat there thoughts of past summers would fill my mind. It was strange how well I could recall almost every detail of past days when I was only a small lad enjoying myself at the beach with my family, or, in more recent years, from when I was thirteen and onwards — and especially summers at school. I remembered how I had tried very hard at school in the first couple of years but when I went up to the third year everything seemed to go to pot. I no longer wanted to waste my time doing homework: there were lots more important things — such as girls, Youth Club and motorbikes. My mate and I bought a scooter between us to use on the dirt track near where I lived, and its arrival brought an added bonus, the attentions of the good looking girls who lived nearby. Those two summers — from thirteen to when I was almost fifteen were two of the greatest summer holidays I had ever enjoyed. We would bomb up and down that field until the last drop of petrol was gone, and often ended up having to push the scooter back home. Mum and Dad were always going to the beach for the day, so when we got back to mine whoever was there just followed me indoors. There were two girls at that time I liked very much: one being Kate and another — well, I'd better not say who the other one was. During those summers I was often lucky enough to find myself in the company of one or the other, which, I might add, was very nice indeed.

Sitting in the garden brought lots of memories that would fill my mind, but as I was only eighteen most of them were of school. Unlike other people I knew I really enjoyed school, especially for the last two or three years. Although I was often in trouble for smoking and so on, there was nothing anyone could really say I had done to hurt anybody. I was lucky enough to be able to get on with most people and so found that I had lots of mates, although I'm sure there must have been some people who hated my guts. But you can't please everyone, that's my motto. I tended to mix with blokes who were a year or two older than me, and as I sat there I wondered what they were all doing nowadays. There was Fred who was going out with Jo, but then there were others, like Terry and Kim, who I had not heard from for a couple of months; then there were Lee, Roger, Phil and the twins who had all been in the year above me when we were at school; then came the lads who were in the same year as myself like Howard, Mervin, Ossie, Whip, Bob, Nigel, Bugs, Chicken, Doorknob, Adrian, Ernie, Trevor, William, and so many more. We had all gone our separate ways once we left that seat of learning, which is inevitable, I suppose, but it would be nice to know what they were all doing now, I thought, as I sat there warming myself in the brilliant sunshine.

During those summer months I not only ventured out into the garden but I had also been down to The Grange with Fred and Jo once or twice. But even though my mates came over and chatted to me it wasn't the same, and when I returned home the feeling of being different or not being able to play pool with them or do other things was very upsetting. I would get upset but then the misery would spur me on to do all the things my friends did.

The summer was over now and the cold wet days were here for the next few months. My daily routine was pretty much the same every day — breakfast, then on the mat for a couple of hours doing my exercises, then lunch, after that back in my bedroom to stand up in my frame for an hour or so, then tea. And that was it — unless I was going out to see some friends later that evening. The days slipped past, running into weeks then months until eventually Christmas came round once again. This year, however, I did not stay in but instead ventured out on Christmas Eve up to the pub with my brother. Later on we moved onto another pub where we met up with my dad and our good friend, Terry. We had a few drinks there and then at about quarter to twelve returned home to pick up Bruce's wife, Jackie, Mum and Lou. While we were collecting them, Terry went home to fetch his wife, Chris and their two children, Jackie and Darren. We all met up outside the local church as we planned to go to Midnight Mass. Once inside, the smell of melting wax filled your nostrils as the whole church was lit up by candles. We sang some hymns and well known carols, then prayed for those less fortunate than ourselves, and by the time the service was over it was getting on for one o'clock.

Mum and Dad invited Chris and Terry back to ours for a drink and hot sausage rolls. We all sat around, drinking and talking until it was almost half past two in the morning. Then Chris and Terry said they had better be getting home to bed because otherwise there would be no point in going. As they left they wished me a Happy Christmas. First Chris, then Jackie kissed me and with that kiss from Jackie I realised that she was no longer a child but a very pretty, very nice young lady. We saw Chris and Terry again over the Christmas period and I also went up to see Kate and her family. Kate and I were still close and both of us still brought presents for each other and for each other's families.

Christmas came and went just like last year but this time at least I found I could open my own presents. Now it was over and a New Year about to begin. With Mr Parker's help, this would be the year when I would walk again.

With the new year came new ideas from Mr Parker on ways to help me improve and get my motionless limbs moving again. Instead of doing exercises in the morning, I was to get out of my chair first thing in the morning after I had had breakfast and not get back into it again until tea time. I was to crawl on my hands and knees up and down, up and down the long corridor in the bungalow from the sitting room to my bedroom, over and over again. Although I had worked hard at my exercises during the year at home they hadn't prepared me for this. At first I found I could only crawl a matter of feet before my arms would give way and I would end up in a heap on the floor. Crawling for me wasn't the simple thing it would have been before my accident: no, it was much harder. First I would get into position on all fours then, leaning a bit onto one knee, I would swing the opposite hip forward and with this movement my knee would automatically drag forward a couple of inches. Then I would move my weight onto that knee, swing the other hip forward and so on. This was how I managed to crawl up and down the lounge, but it was several weeks before I could finally make it down to my bedroom then back into the lounge. After the first couple of weeks, though, I found my knees were becoming the worse for wear through the punishment that I was dishing out to them. At first the skin became red, then as I crawled more and more it broke and became very sore. I had to give up the crawling for a time so that my knees could heal up again. In the meantime I went back to doing my exercises and after a week or so my knees were very much better. Dad suggested I bought some elastic knee pads to fit under my jeans which would help prevent the same thing happening again. So, armed with plasters and knee pads I started again in earnest. Up and down the hall, from the lounge to the bedroom, time after time until I could physically take no more and my arms had turned to jelly and neither love nor money would hold me up a minute longer. Doing this new kind of therapy left me very tired indeed as you can well imagine and after tea it was all I could do to keep my eyes open until I finally had to give in and go off to bed.

As I crawled more and more over the coming weeks then months it became much easier. Mr Parker told me that once I got to the end of the hall and into the lounge I must pull myself up into one of the arm chairs and do ten press-ups, then get out of the chair, back onto the floor and crawl to my bedroom again; once there, pull myself up onto my bed, transfer into my wheelchair and do ten press-ups in that. When they were done I had to get back out of the chair, back onto the floor and crawl back to the lounge and repeat the whole thing again and again until I had done it ten times. I did not argue but did as I was asked. Up and down the hall I went, only stopping from time to time to take a breather. As I did so I was breathing in the dust from the carpets and a feeling of sickness churned within my stomach. I asked myself, 'Is it worth going through this day after day?' The same reply always came back: 'Of course it is, if it's going to make me walk. I have got to keep going, I must keep going.' I kept telling myself over and over again.

Not only was I crawling, but Mr Parker arranged for me to go for a swim in the pool of a friend he had treated in the past. We pulled up in the yard of the farm where this chap lived, and as I was getting out of the car he came over to introduce himself.

'Hello, my name's Hugh,' he said, as he sat in his wheelchair watching me get out of the car into mine.

'Hello, I'm Andy,' I replied. 'Oh, and thanks for letting me come over and use your pool.'

'That's OK. Come on, I'll show you the way.'

Mr Parker was also there so he, my father and I followed Hugh along a path to a building at the back of the farm. As we went in the door we saw first a small room with a padded work bench where he must do his exercises. Standing in the corner was a set of parallel bars. Hugh opened another door and through it was the pool with most of the far side of the wall completely made of glass. Mr Parker and Hugh stayed in there while Dad helped me to change. Mr Parker had also got his trunks on and he and Dad lifted me out of my chair and sat me on the side of the pool. Mr Parker got into the water and lifted me into it with him. We were in the shallow end so he got me to try and stand up and see if I could take a couple of steps.

'That's right,' he said trying to give me all the encouragement that he could. I don't know if I took a step or not but if I didn't it wasn't from lack of effort.

Then he said, 'How about a bit of a swim?' That's what I was there for so why not? The last time I had swum was when I was in hospital and that was almost eighteen months ago. Mr Parker laid me on my back and as I moved my arms the way I had been taught I found that I had not lost the ability to swim.

'That's it,' I heard Mr Parker say, 'Keep it going, I'll swim alongside you. We'll go up to the far end and back again.' There I was, my head back and my arms working well but as I got to the far end of the pool they were really getting tired.

'I've got to have a rest,' I shouted out.

'Look above you! See that rope with the knot in the end of it? Reach up and grab a hold of that if you want a rest,' was Mr Parker's reply.

I did as he said but missed it first time and went under, taking a little bit of extra water in. Then somehow I got hold of it and hung on for dear life. While I lay there, floating but still hanging on to the rope, Mr Parker swam over to the side. Several minutes passed until finally I heard him say, 'OK, then, you can start back now.'

The only trouble was, I wasn't sure that I could make it back to the shallow end and was reluctant to let go of the rope.

'I can't let go. I'm not sure I will get back to the shallow end!' I shouted out.

'Well, if you don't let go you'll have to hang on there all day,' came Mr Parker's answer.

There was no reply to that so, after taking a deep breath, I let go and began to swim back to the other end. I started well, then my arms began to tire very quickly until eventually they ground to a stop and I started to sink very fast. As my head inevitably went under I began to take in more water. This time there was nothing to grab hold of and I began to panic, which brought the thought of drowning to my mind. Suddenly I felt myself being lifted up and as my head came back out of the water I gasped and spluttered all over the place. 'OK, I've got you,' I heard Mr Parker say. Then swimming with me he took me over to the side where I hung on still gasping for breath and very frightened.

'That will do for today, I think,' he said and lifted me out of the water. He and Dad helped me back into my chair and then it was just a matter of Mr Parker going back to the other room to get changed. Once dressed, he came in with Hugh.

'You did very well,' they both said.

'Thanks, but I was pretty frightened when I went under,' I replied. With that they all laughed, including Dad.

Dad got me dressed, and afterwards Mr Parker said, 'Now you realise how much stronger you have to get. Hugh, show him what I mean.' Hugh wheeled himself up to the parallel bars and, without letting his feet touch the floor, moved along the full length of the bars using just his arms. 'That's what I want you to be able to do eventually,' said Mr Parker as Hugh got back into his chair. It had certainly been an eye opener going there that day and on the way home I realised that I had still got a lot more hard work in front of me.

Chapter 18
Hypnosis

The visit to Hugh's pool was the only one I ever made in the end, for a couple of reasons really; one was that it was a good twenty miles from where I lived and another was that Mr Parker could not spare the time to meet me over there during the week. Although swimming was out, something else was to come into my life in the very near future. I had religiously kept on at my exercises, plus the crawling, but although I had got much stronger no real movement had returned to my paralysed muscles. Then, on Wednesday, I found myself lying as usual on that piece of foam on Mr Parker's dining room table. He had just put me through my paces and was manipulating my neck. At this point I should explain that since the first couple of visits when he only gently touched my neck, he had increased the movement over the last eighteen months so that now he would vigorously turn my head to every conceivable position, bar turning it a full three hundred and sixty degrees. As a result I had now lost all fear of ever breaking my neck again. As he finished off this time, though, he pulled out one of the chairs and sat down to have a chat with me before I left.

'I just can't understand why you haven't got any movement back yet,' he said. 'Your neck is fine now. All I can think of is that you've got a mental block of some sort.'

I turned my head and looked straight at him. 'There is nobody who wants to walk more than I do,' I blurted out.

'No, consciously there probably isn't, but sub-consciously your brain is either frightened to let you walk again as the last memory it has is that accident, or it's saying, "Oh well, we don't want to walk again because we will have to get up early and go to work and also have to fend for ourselves again and so on." '

As he spoke, I realised what he was saying made sense. 'Well, what can I do to change the way my sub-conscious mind thinks?' I asked.

'I've been thinking about that,' he answered. 'How do you feel about trying a hypnotist, to see if he can put you under hypnosis then talk to your sub-conscious? Also, while you're under hypnosis he could ask you to move your legs, and that way we could find out if it was your mind stopping you from walking or if it was something else.'

'I'll try anything, you know that, to get me walking again,' I replied.

'OK, leave it with me and I will get in touch with someone by the time you come back next week.'

When I returned the following week Mr Parker told me he had been unable to find anyone willing to do what he wanted. The strange thing was that if I'd wanted to give up smoking or lose weight well, then of course they would help me, but something worthwhile — no way! He tried again the following week, phoning all over the place, even to Harley Street in London, but still no joy. Then when I returned for my next visit he told me that he had bought a book and was going to learn how to practise hypnosis himself. He had started by preparing a tape for me to listen to once I returned home. I was to listen to this every morning before I did my exercises, it wasn't a way of hypnotising me but just a way of relaxing my mind so he could talk to me and encourage me while I was at home and also have more contact with me than just the half hour that he saw me on Wednesday.

I took the tape home with me. The following morning lying on my mattress I plugged in the tape recorder and placed my head phones on so that all I could hear was his voice. It started off with Mr Parker telling me to let my body relax completely, then in my mind to see my body from the tips of my toes to the top of my head; then to imagine that the messages from my brain were travelling down all the nerves in my spinal cord and reaching their destinations and were now making all my muscles, limbs, joints and ligaments respond to all that I was asking of them. After that he talked about how the accident wasn't my fault, it could have happened to anyone and that if I was to get well again there would be almost no chance of the same thing ever happening again. Then there was a clicking, signalling the end of the tape. From now on I listened to this tape every morning before starting my exercises. In a way it was conditioning my mind to really believe in myself and to try that bit harder.

Several weeks passed which found me carrying on the way I always had, plus the extra help from the tape that Mr Parker had given me. It was on yet another Wednesday when I was at his house once again for my weekly check up, that he greeted me with some good news: 'I've found a hypnotist who will see you,' he said as Dad and his wife carried me into the room.

'Oh great! How far away?' I replied.

'That's the funny thing: I have been phoning all over the place, London, Cambridge, Oxford and so on with no joy. Then I happened to notice an ad in the local paper — you know, ''Hypnotist able to stop smoking and help lose weight'' and I thought ''Why not ring him? He can only say no.'' But he didn't. On the contrary, after I explained what I wanted him to do with you he said ''OK, fine. Tell him to give me a ring and make an appointment.'' '

'At last,' I thought, 'perhaps he can find a way to get my

brain to send messages through my millions of nerves to every part of my body and make them work for me once more.'

That afternoon, after leaving Mr Parker's and returning home, I immediately phoned the hypnotist, a Mr Howorth, making an appointment for Friday afternoon. The next couple of days shot past in anticipation of the visit. Dad parked the car on the opposite side of the road, next to the park. After getting me out of the car he pushed me across to the house Mr Howorth used for his practice. We rang the bell and an oldish man answered the door.

'Hello,' he said, 'you must be Andrew. Please come in.'

Dad lifted both me and my chair up the couple of steps and then pushed me down the short hallway and into a small room. Once in there Mr Howorth explained that he did not live there, but merely rented the ground floor from Monday to Friday. Both he and Dad sat down and then he asked me the usual questions: how had I had the accident and how long was I in hospital? Then he told me what he and Mr Parker had spoken about on the phone. 'OK, that's about it then. Well, if you would like to get into this chair I think you will be able to relax a lot better.' It was one of those Parker Knoll chairs which reclined and also lifted your feet up so that you were almost lying down. I transferred myself into it and made myself comfortable. 'If you would like to sit in the other room for a little while, Mr Tricker. It will be easier for Andrew to relax,' he said to Dad.

After Dad had closed the door he sat and talked to me a lot more before standing up and moving directly behind me. 'OK, Andy. That is right — you do prefer being called Andy?'

'Yes, that's right,' I replied.

'OK. Now then. Look up at the bridge of my nose, concentrate hard, keep looking, your eyes are closing, they are getting heavier and heavier, now they're closed.

I let my eyes close and just listened to his voice as he asked.

Then he told me that my eyes were getting heavy, so heavy, and this feeling was spreading from my eyes down to my arms and making them feel so heavy. When he lifted my arm up it would do exactly as he said it would. He told me to concentrate on my legs and said that they were becoming warm and were starting to tingle. As I lay there, completely relaxed, it felt as he said.

Then he told me, 'Now, Andy, move your right leg. Do you see it moving, just a little bit? Come on, move it up just a fraction.' In that relaxed state of mind I could see this picture of my leg moving, but in reality could not feel it lifting up. Then he asked me to try and move my left leg or foot, and again it was the same feeling.

'OK, Andy. Now I'm going to count to five and when I reach the number five you will open your eyes, feeling completely awake and alert but relaxed and confident. One, two, three, four, five! Open your eyes. That's right. Feeling OK? Did you enjoy your sleep?'

I blinked my eyes several times, like you do first thing in the morning so that they can adjust to the light once again.

'Was it all right?' I asked.

'Did you think it was OK?' he replied.

'Yer, it was good, only I thought when you were hypnotised you went right out and didn't hear a thing. But I could hear every word you said.'

He explained that not everyone went out completely and could not remember anything; but instead some went into a very relaxed state like me, but at the same time could still recall all that had taken place. We talked a bit longer, then he placed me under hypnosis a couple more times before asking Dad to come back. He then explained all that he had done and Dad asked, 'Do you think you can help Andy in any way?'

Mr Howorth paused for a moment. 'Yes, I believe I can,' he replied, 'but we will just have to see over the coming weeks.' I got back into my wheelchair and all that was left for me to do was make another appointment for the following week and pay up my ten pounds for today's session.

The weeks now found Dad taking me into town twice: first to Mr Parker's on Wednesdays then to the hypnotist's on Fridays. All in all it was becoming quite expensive, but using my disability pension in this way did not bother me as long as they were genuinely helping me to improve. I suppose I went to Mr Howorth's for nearly three months, and he never did anything different from the first session, and I never made any real improvement. Then, one day, when we arrived, he introduced us to a younger chap who by coincidence had the same Christian name as myself. Mr Howorth explained that this chap, Andrew, was starting up in town and had read in some journal about a man who had used hypnosis to walk again after a serious accident. He wondered if from now on I would like to see Andrew rather than himself. I agreed. The only trouble with this new arrangement was that Andrew's practice was on the second floor and there were some very steep steps to climb. To get over this Dad and I had to ask our friend, Terry, and on some occasions my brother-in-law, John, to come along with us so that they could help Dad lift me up the stairs. I ended up going to Andrew for several months, but all to no avail. Looking back, I suppose all they had done was to pass me from one to the other, and in doing so had both succeeded in taking a considerable sum of money from me. And the funny thing about both of them was that their methods were very similar, and although they had said that I had been hypnotised, I am still convinced that I hadn't been.

Chapter 19
Managing Alone

It was around this time that Mum and Dad wanted to go and visit some of my relations up in the north, a good two or three hundred miles away. As my sister, Jo, was now married there would be no one at home with me. One evening, as they sat talking about it, I suddenly had a brain wave.

'Why don't you let me stay on my own? That way I could find out if I could cope, because, let's face it, one day I will have to.'

At first they flatly refused and said that I wouldn't be able to manage, which I resented a great deal. Over the last year or so I had improved no end, to the point where I was now almost completely independent, all except needing a little help on the loo every other day and that could easily be remedied by calling the local district nurse. Although I did not like the idea of Sister Trimm coming to see after me, I was grown up enough to realise that Mum and Dad weren't going to live forever and if the worst came to the worst and I was still in the wheelchair I'd have to have someone to come in and help me. We talked about it a bit more, Mum asking whether I could do this and that until I finally said, 'Look, Mum, I can get myself up, washed and dressed in the mornings, I can make myself a drink and something to eat whenever I am hungry and I can also get myself undressed and into bed at night, so what else is there that I have to be able to do to stay on my own?'

She thought for a moment. 'What about cooking your food?' she said. 'You haven't done that before and you will be so alone.'

'I can cook myself a baked potato and grill bacon, sausages and chops. I can have oven chips and fruit and ice cream for a sweet,' I said. 'Anyway it's not as if you're going to be away for a month — you will only be gone five or six days. As for being alone, Judy's only just up the road and she will be calling in every day. Then there's Kate and Chris and Terry. I'll be fine.'

Mum said no more but, 'We'll see.'

The subject was dropped, but later that week I asked Mr Parker what he thought and he agreed that it would be a great opportunity for me to see if I could cope on my own. That evening Dad talked it over again with Mum until she finally agreed that I should be given the chance, and so they arranged to go up to my cousins in two weeks' time.

The two weeks slipped past quickly, and suddenly it was the morning of their departure. Mum went through everything once more, checking that I had this and that and would not want for anything while they were away. I watched as they got into the car and wondered to myself if I had done the right thing, asking to be alone. But there was no going back now: I was waving goodbye to them as they pulled away and drove off down the road. Now that they had gone that old familiar feeling returned — the same feeling I had when they left me during the time I was in hospital. However, after a few minutes it gently slipped away as I got on with doing things, such as getting the different items out that I would need for my evening meal. The day passed slowly by. My sister, Judy, called during the afternoon to make sure I was OK and to remind me that if there were any problems in the night I was to call her. That evening Mum called to tell me that they had arrived all right and also to check on how I was doing.

'What did you have for tea?' she asked.

'Well,' I told her. 'I had oven chips, grilled fish fingers and tinned peas for my firsts and a yoghurt for a sweet.'

'Everything work out OK?'

'Not too bad. I dropped one of my fish fingers on the floor but since you had cleaned it before leaving I picked it up and put it back on my plate again.'

'Oh, Andy, you're dreadful,' Mum replied. Then after chatting a bit longer we ran out of things to say and so said goodbye to one another until she phoned later on in the week. I went into the lounge and sat and watched the telly, then went off to the bathroom and got ready for bed. On the way through I made sure all the lights were out and the back door was locked. Once settled in bed I lay there in the dark and for the first time it dawned on me that I was completely alone. It was strange how every creak and sound seemed to echo in my mind. What if someone broke in? What would I do? There was no way I could get up and run away or stand and fight him off. All I could do would be to say, 'Take what you want, but just leave me alone.' What about if a fire started? This I knew was one of Mum and Dad's greatest worries. If the phone was still working I could call the fire brigade quickly and Judy and John who would soon come to my rescue. It was a real comfort to have a phone right beside my bed, knowing that if anything should happen I could call somebody. Thinking about this relieved some of my fears and enabled me to drop off to sleep. Mind you, that wasn't one of the best night's sleep that I had ever had as I continually kept waking up at the slightest sound that the bungalow made during that long night.

The following morning I woke to the alarm on my watch. Letting myself wake up completely, I got out of bed into my chair and pushed off up to the bathroom. After getting washed and dressed I went into the kitchen and made a pot of tea and some toast for my breakfast. It was now becoming apparent to me how much Mum really did for me each and every day, now that I was having to do everything for myself — like making tea, getting my things ready for the following morning, getting my food ready for the day ahead and keeping the place reasonably clean and tidy. Those five (nearly six) days that I spent on my own were really good for me, although I never quite got used to the nights. My cooking, on the other hand, became much better as each day passed; also, the fear of not seeing anybody from one day to the next never arose as my sister, Judy, called in every day to check that I was OK and then the district nurse, Sister Trimm, arrived every other day. Also, I had a visit from Terry and Chris's daughter, Jackie, one evening which was very nice. Kate came down on another night so all in all I saw more people that week than I did when my parents were at home.

Mum, Dad and Lou arrived home on the Monday. They had rung me almost every day while they were away, making sure I was OK so there wasn't anything to tell them that I hadn't already told them on the phone — except that I'd coped fine. Those six days on my own had seen me overcome yet another hurdle and I now knew that if anything unforeseen did happen to my parents I could live on my own. This really helped to take away the fear that if I should still be in this wheelchair when my parents couldn't look after me any more, I wouldn't have to face the inevitability of being put in some home.

I had had the accident over three years ago and although I had come a long way from the days when I couldn't even lift my arms up from the sheets on the bed to the point where I was almost completely independent, my goal — or my dream of walking again — still hadn't been fulfilled. There was no giving up on my part and yet another new year found me trying yet another hypnotist. This time I travelled up to London to a top class place called Upper Wimpole Street which ran parallel to Harley Street. This time I saw an Indian chap. Although he was very good at hypnotising me and I went to see him a couple of times, it was all to no avail. The reason I only went twice was the fact that it took a good two to two and a half hours to get there and then he charged me forty pounds for each session. When he told me he would have to see me every week there was no way I could afford it. In addition there was the more than likely possibility that I would have gone to him for several months and in the end I would still have been no better off physically.

So, I gave up on hypnosis as a possible way of getting my muscles back. Then I heard of another form of medical treatment, Chiropractice. This was an American treatment, run by a father and son partnership from their home on the outskirts of the local town. I booked an appointment and on my first visit met the son; he talked to me and asked how I had had the accident, then took me into another room where my neck was X-rayed — the first time since I had left hospital. The following week I went back and he showed me the X-Ray, pointing out the vertebrae that had been squashed in the whip lashing of my neck from the accident. He then went on to explain that, as I had got feeling over my body, the nerves could not have been severed, so he would do all he could to help me. Over the weeks and eventually months I visited him, he used two pieces of equipment. First, there was a sort of staple gun which he would place at given points near my neck. When he pressed it it would push into my neck. He said this was helping to free the nerves; then there was a kind of box on which I had to lay my head. Without warning the lid of the box would suddenly close, with the result that my head suddenly dropped and my neck cricked, first one way, then the other. I kept going to them for several months, in the hope that one day after I left there my nerves would suddenly be free and the messages from my brain would once again be able to get through to my muscles and limbs. But once again my hopes and wishes did not come true: it had been yet another red herring. I had tried, but unfortunately Chiropractice, like hypnosis, had not worked out the way I'd wanted it to.

When Chiropractice failed I became very disheartened about everything and in everyone — even my association with Mr Parker finally came to an end. There was no bad feeling on my part towards him because he hadn't been able to get me walking again as he had said he would. I was sad and upset, of course, but I realised that if I had never met him there was no way that I would be in the position I now was; almost completely independent, having the confidence to stay on my own and also having a total belief inside myself that one day there would be a way for me to get my limbs going again. He had given me all those things and more: if I had never met him I would still be relying on Mum and Dad to do all those things for me that they did when I first came home. Moreover, I'd probably still be frightened to move my head in case I broke my neck once again. No, we had both come to realise that he had done as much as he could for me and if I still kept going to him we would end up just going through the motions without getting any further forward. But no longer going to see Mr Parker did not mean the end of everything he had taught me, and to this very day you will find me every morning in my bedroom for about two hours doing the sequence of exercises he made me do from our very first meetings. I am sure that's the reason I have kept so healthy, and if an operation was to become available tomorrow I know that I would be in perfect shape to have it done. So, although he didn't get me walking again, I still owe Mr Parker so much.

Chapter 20
Please, Never Give up Trying

Athough I still did my exercises every day my life seemed to have no meaning. It was as if I was just going through the motions, the one thing I always dreaded happening, even when I was still going to Mr Parker's. I had got to find new interests that would help me overcome this depression. Mum and Dad had bought me all the things I would need to start painting in oils the previous Christmas and, although I was no Rembrandt, it gave me something to do and at the same time took my mind off myself. I had another hobby: backing horses. Dad had got me an account over at the local bookies, so now each morning I was able to phone my bets through. My outlay was only about fifty pence to a pound a day and if the racing was on the telly it was a great way of spending an afternoon. The enjoyment that I got from watching horses racing and having my brother living at Newmarket, the centre of British horse racing, prompted me to actually go to one of the main meetings that was held there. The first year Dad took me up by car and my brother brought me back in the evening. It was quite an achievement for me to go somewhere where there were literally thousands of people, but after getting over my initial nerves I really enjoyed myself. The following year Dad couldn't take me for some reason, so if I really wanted to go I knew I would have to go by train — which is what I did.

Dad was able to drive me to the station. I was taken across to the platform in the parcel lift and then Dad and one of the porters lifted me into the guard's van. Dad stayed with me until just before the train pulled out, then said goodbye. It was the first time that I had been on a train since my accident and because my muscles didn't work any more I found my legs swinging from side to side with the motion of the train as it picked up speed. As it slowed down at each station I found that if I didn't hold on tight I felt as if I would end up on the floor. After overcoming these problems, there I was, sitting quietly on my own, enjoying the view of the countryside from the dirty window at my side. It did not bother me having to sit in the guard's van and the look of surprise on people's faces as they brought their bikes on board was quite enjoyable really. It was as if you could hear their brains saying, 'What on earth is he doing in here?' The journey only took about an hour and Bruce was there to meet me at the other end. We went across to the pub and, after a couple of drinks and something to eat, went on to the races. A good day was had by both of us, I believe, and that evening Bruce and my sister-in-law, Jackie, took me back home and stayed for the rest of the weekend. All in all, I have been to Newmarket for four years running and last time made both trips, there and back again, by train. I had to do this as my brother and his wife have divorced. This was a very sad thing, not only for them but for the whole family; but it is inevitable, I suppose, when two people have got so much pride that neither will give in.

Not only did I venture out to the race course during the year after I finished seeing Mr Parker, but I also made friends again with my old mate, Bob. He started to come round regularly, taking me out all over the village, up through the church lanes, down to the river and round to the social club for a drink at lunch times. After he had been coming round and taking me out, sometimes two or three times a week, for a whole summer, he suggested one day that we called in to see his mum and dad. We were sitting in their lounge, just chatting, when Bob's mum mentioned a young lad who lived on their estate who was going to see a couple of faith healers. She asked if I had ever thought of going to someone like that.

'I can't say I have, Mrs Hammond,' I said.

'Well, this boy suffers from eczema and all sorts of other complaints and apparently these people have done him the world of good,' she explained.

This got me thinking: 'There would be no harm in trying,' I thought. 'It can't hurt me in any way and, who knows, they might be able to do me a lot of good.' I asked Mrs Hammond if she could find out their address for me and a couple of days later Bob brought it down with their name and telephone number. So that evening I got on the telephone and arranged to see them at the end of the week. Instead of telling Mum and Dad about them, I thought that if I could get someone else to take me and they laid their hands on me and a miracle happened and I came out walking, what a fantastic surprise it would be for them.

Unfortunately, my dream did not become reality. When I arrived, I found they lived in an ordinary council house on one of the big estates in the local town. They invited me to their lounge. Like everyone else, they asked me how the accident happened and then explained that all they would do was lay their hands on me and healing powers would pass from them through into me. They stood around me first laying their hands on my head, then placing them on my back, arms, hands and legs. They were an oldish couple but seemed very pleasant. After they had finished I asked if I owed them any money.

'We don't ask people for money,' they replied, 'but if you'd like to give us a little something towards our heating bill that's entirely up to you.' I put my hand into my pocket and gave them a couple of pounds and arranged to see them the following week. This first week Mr Hammond had taken me and then the following week my sister, Jo, took me — all without Mum and Dad knowing. After the first two visits, though, when nothing had happened I finally told them where I had been and the reason I wanted it to be a surprise. They didn't mind too much, I don't think, and now they knew Dad took me the following week. All in all I suppose I visited the healers for several weeks before calling it a day.

That old couple were not the only faith healers I turned to in the hope that maybe one of them might be able to improve me in some way. I will never forget one healing service held at a small church on the outskirts of town. A well-known healer was coming, and there I was, sitting in the second row from the front. In front of me, though, was this youngish man who was even worse off than me and as I sat behind him I thought, 'Well, if there's anyone who deserves to be healed, he does.' The church soon filled up to the point where a few extra chairs had to be brought in and then the service began with a few songs. A man got up to deliver his sermon, which was greeted every so often with cries of 'Halleluiah.' Then the well known healer started at the front row, laying his hands on those who wanted him to. As he worked his way along, in my mind I was saying, 'Please, Lord, let this man heal me with his hands. Please, Lord, let this come true.' By the time he had reached me I'd watched him lay his hands on the young chap in front of me with no effect at all; then he moved onto an oldish man who had got trouble with his legs and could only walk with sticks. When he touched him, he told him to jump up and the old man did exactly as he was told, then started crying with joy because he hadn't been able to stand without using his sticks for almost ten years. I heard the healer say, 'Your turn.' Then he laid his hands on my forehead and called out, 'Please, Lord, through me heal this young man sitting here, make him walk again.' I closed my eyes. There was no change: I was still sitting in this rotten wheelchair. The healer moved on to the next person and it was all over. Today wasn't going to be the day that the miracle which I prayed so hard for was going to happen. Again I would return home no different from when I left.

It was after trying things like the faith healing and hypnotists that I would become very depressed. It wasn't because I'd tried them, it was because they hadn't worked. See, you can't help thinking whenever you're going to try something new that this is the thing that is going to work for you and everything's going to be fine again, but when it doesn't work out the way you had imagined it would be in your dreams in the days or weeks before, well, then of course you're disappointed. It is easy to say, 'Well, you shouldn't expect too much. You must not pin your hopes too high on this person,' but if you don't believe that he is going to do you some good and you're not in the right frame of mind, then there is no point in going. It is just a vicious circle. But after having tried so many things it was becoming increasingly harder to get myself in the right frame of mind whenever I heard of someone or something new that might be worth trying.

It was when I was feeling particularly down that an old friend called to see me whom I hadn't seen for some time: his name was Tony and the last time that I had seen him was while I was in hospital. I had become friends with him as well as others such as Sylvia and another Tony when Kate and I were in the Appeal Theatre group in Ipswich. It wasn't really my scene, moving the props, etc, between each scene but actually getting involved changed my attitude and I had begun to enjoy it very much. Anyway, this Tony had come to tell me that the members of the group had collected some money for me and wondered if there was anything that I particularly wanted. There was nothing that sprang to mind, so Tony suggested one of those TV games that would be good therapy for my hands. I thanked him and also wrote a letter thanking all those who kindly contributed towards it. When he visited me again some weeks later he happened to tell me about his parents who were also healers and asked if I would like to go and see them. I wasn't too sure at first and told him that I had already seen a couple of different healers without anything happening. Anyway he told me to think about it and finally I decided that there was nothing to lose so I would go. I ended up going to see them every week for over a year and both his mum and step-dad where really nice. For the first time I experienced something in his mother's hands when she placed them on my head and legs. There was this strange heat that passed from her into me and a sense of calmness would come over me whenever I visited them, but although she had this strange gift or power it was not enough to get me to improve in the physical sense. In spite of the fact that they hadn't been able to perform a great miracle, I gained something else through going to them: it was as if I could now live with the way I was. Don't get me wrong, I hadn't given up on getting completely well again: it was just that I had become more at ease with myself and able to cope with life much better than I had before I had met them. They hadn't preached to me — on the contrary, they hardly ever brought religion into the conversation, but I'm sure in my own mind that they truly had some marvellous gift. Anyway, like I said, I ended up going to see them for over a year until Tony's step-dad had a stroke and they could no longer carry on giving healing; but I will be eternally grateful to them for what they gave me.

Soon after I stopped seeing these latest healers, Kate and I finally cut the last thread that had been holding our relationship together. She had been married for just over a year, but somehow we still remained close friends. Whenever she visited her parents I would either go up and see her there or she would come down to mine before she returned home. We had stayed close even though she had married, and I think the reason was because I would listen and try and understand whenever she had a problem. But the break happened just after Christmas. We had seen each other quite a lot up to then and on Christmas Eve exchanged presents. I didn't see her over Christmas like I had done on previous years as she obviously had to spend it with her husband, so Christmas passed and the New Year arrived. The months slipped by until it got to over six months since the last time I saw her. This cut me up inside because I couldn't think what I had done to stop her from wanting to come and see me. She's never been to see me again and the only thing I can think is that either she got fed up with coming to see me or, the most obvious reason, her husband objected and she stopped to prevent arguments between them. Although my relationship with Kate has ended, I have been lucky enough to stay good friends with the rest of her family which I cherish very much.

In the years that have passed since my accident I have learnt a great deal about myself and other people. For instance, before my accident I thought that money was everything. I remember thinking when I was at work how hard done by I was not having enough money to buy a car, or even to last me over the week once I had been out for a drink at the weekend. If a little windfall should come my way, I thought, what a great difference it would make to my life. Here I am now, with nearly three thousand pounds in the bank, that I have been able to save over the last five years, but I am far worse off now than I have ever been. It's strange as I sit here and listen to other people moaning about how hard up they are, if only they realised how much richer they were than an awful lot of people in this world. It amazes me how much preference people give to material things like owning their houses, having the best furniture and buying a new car just to stand it out in front of their homes so that everyone can see it. Although it is nice to have these things, and for those who haven't got any more than a roof over their heads they are good things to dream about, to me they are nice but not essential. To me someone who is well off or rich is the person who has his health and has also got lots of friends and people who like or love him. I look at it like this: a new car or a three piece suite can't listen to you when you're low or show you any affection and they cannot come and visit you when you're ill in hospital or lying on your death bed. Lots of people lead a very lonely existence because they have considered possessions to be more important than friends. So now I would like to thank all those who have been my friends over these last few years, as without the love and friendship that they have given me and still give me there is no way I could have made it through the months after the accident and go on living. Although sometimes I might not show it, I am forever in their debt.

I still have a loving family and friends who call round to see me regularly, but of course I miss having a relationship with someone of the opposite sex. For one thing, I miss the sexual side of a relationship, but there are other things too: like sharing your life with another person, continually giving and receiving affection from one another; being able to talk and go out to different places with each other; to care for and love that person and be cared for and loved in return and, finally, (which I know is going to sound corny) to grow old together. At the moment I don't go out much to meet people, but even if I did I doubt that I would find anyone who was daft enough to take me on and since it's been so long since I have chatted anyone up I doubt that I would get past the first hurdle. Just supposing though, that I did meet someone who took a liking to me and we found we could talk to each other and enjoyed each other's company; then, one night, we found ourselves alone and it was up to me to make a move — by the time I had undone her bra catch or the top button on her blouse it would be gone midnight and time for her to leave. Or say I had my own place and she asked to stay the night: just as were going to make our way to the bedroom I'd have to say 'Hang on a minute, just got to go to the bathroom to take this bag off.' That would really turn her on. If there is a lady out there for me she would have to be very understanding and very, very special indeed to fall in love with someone like myself, and even if we got to the stage where we made love it would have to be her who did all the work and be on top — come to think of it, that might be nice. If I did find someone who loved me and wanted to spend her life with me, then we would have to decide whether to marry or live together. I think I would rather live with her, so she always had the opportunity to leave if things started to go wrong or she found that life with me was not what she wanted after all. Hypothetically, though, if I did have a relationship with someone and it didn't work out I do not think there would be any bad feeling or hatred on my part — only understanding and fondness towards her for giving it a try.

I am now drawing to the end of my book. As you have read my words you must have got a picture of me as an ordinary lad who was at work and attending college, until that fateful day when, leaving college, he hit a lorry and turned his life upside down and inside out. You have travelled with me through all my experiences in hospital and met all my family and the friends who comforted me and never left me down all through that difficult time. Then you have been with me during the time that I have been home, and read about my struggle to get back the use of my muscles and limbs by going to see all kinds of different people, osteopaths, hypnotists, Chiropractics, faith healers and just healers. I would like to say at this point there is no one who could have been a better father than I have had. He has taken me everywhere in search of a cure and has helped me so much, more than any words could say. Then there's my mum, who has loved and cared for me over these last years like no mother could have done and still remains the kindest, loveliest person that I know. Then there is my little sister, Lou. Well, she is not so little any more but even though she is growing up she has been just great all the time and is always there if I need her. There is one other person without whose love and encouragement through those months in hospital, I could not have got through and that is Kate, of course. Then there are so many friends who have been so kind — Chris, Terry and their two children, Jackie and Darren, Kate's family — George and Dot, my old mates, Terry, Bob and Howard who came and saw me regularly. Then there is Sylvia who has written to me regularly over the years. These are only a few. To all of them I take this opportunity of saying thank you, and to the rest of my family — brother Bruce, sisters, Bren, Judy, Jo and all their husbands and families. I thank you all for being you.

It has taken me nearly twelve months to write this book, or type it, anyway, with just two index fingers, but I hope you've enjoyed it and I'd just like to say: if you who are reading this book are suffering in some way, please never give up trying. I hope to walk again one day, and that's a dream I'll never give up on.

Other Titles in the Adlib Series

Terry Edge
Fanfare For a Teenage Warrior In Love
In two and a half extraordinary weeks at Hornford Comprehensive Tom Hall falls in love, becomes a T.V 'personality', gets caught up in a school betting shop, plays championship football — and survives with flying colours.   233 98080 6

Will Gatti
Berry Moon
An old family feud explodes into violence in the west of Ireland.
233 97828 3

Dennis Hamley
The Fourth Plane At The Flypast
A tragedy from the Second World War reaches out to affect the lives of Sue and John and their family.   233 97788 0

Haunted United
A ghostly footballer stalks the grounds of Bowland United.
233 97942 5

The Shirt Off A Hanged Man's Back
Tales of the supernatural.   233 97650 7

Michael Hardcastle
No Defence
Where does a brilliant, young footballer go for his kicks?
233 97912 3

Minfong Ho
Rice Without Rain
Famine in a Thai village make an insecure background for Ned and Jinda's uneasy romance.   233 97911 5

Pete Johnson
Catch You On The Flipside
A sharp, lighthearted look at what happens to a boy, accustomed to girls falling for him, when he falls in love himself.   233 98074 1

Secrets From The School Underground
To find out what's really going on at Farndale Comprehensive you have to 'read' the writing on the wall behind the bike shed —a sort of unofficial school newspaper.   233 97987 5

Rhodri Jones
Different Friends
It was learning the truth about Azhar that shocked Chris into changing his attitude to love, making him think for the first time, what the word really meant.   233 98096 2

Getting It Wrong
If you're young and black, it is very easy to 'get it wrong' as Clive and Donovan find out.   233 97910 7

Hillsden Riots
What happens when the frustrations of young black people become intolerable.   233 97827 5

Geraldine Kaye
A Breath Of Fresh Air
Amy's interest in a school project on slavery becomes a reality when she slips back in time to experience life as a black slave in eighteenth century Jamaica.   233 98163 9

Elizabeth Mace
Beware The Edge
The perils of dabbing in the supernatural.   233 97908 5

Boxes
Rona Goodall is an old maid of eighteen and desperate for a boyfriend. Along comes Sean and her problems seem to be solved.   233 97670 1

The Goodall Family Games
An earlier story of Rona and her family.   233 97551 9

Suzanne Newton
I Will Call It Georgie's Blues
Bitter family tension threatens the youngest son of a preacher in the American Deep South.   233 97720 1

Eduardo Quiroga
On Foreign Ground
A young Argentinian soldier in the Falklands remembers his love affair with an English girl.   233 97909 3

Caryl Rivers
Virgins
A bitter-sweet story of American high school girls growing up in the fifties.   233 97791 0

Margaret Simpson
The Drug Smugglers
Paul decides to track down the drug pushers who are supplying his sister.   233 97673 6

Rosemary Wells
The Man In The Woods
Is he an ordinary hooligan or a more sinister figure mysteriously connected with events of the American Civil War of a hundred years ago?   233 97785 6

When No One Was Looking
Young American tennis star, Kathy Bardy, resents her new rival but she didn't expect her to die.   233 97669 8